The North Herring

The North Herring Fishing

Ring-net Fishermen in the Minches

ANGUS MARTIN

British Cataloguing in Publication Data
A catalogue record for this book is available
from the British Library

ISBN 1 899863 80 X

Typeset by XL Publishing Services, Tiverton.
Printed in Great Britain by SRP Ltd, Exeter
for House of Lochar, Isle of Colonsay, Argyll PA61 7YR

Contents

· · · · · · · · · · · · · ·

Illustrations

Maps

Plates (between pages 86 and 87)
The crew of the *Watchful*, 1969.
Per Matt Sloan, Maidens

The four McDougall brothers of Tarbert and crews, c 1935.
Per Peter McDougall, Tarbert

The *Stella Maris* in the sea-lock at Crinan, her neighbour the *Fiona* ahead of her.
Photograph by Tom Weir

Sammy Gemmell's *Storm Drift*, entering Dunure harbour at the end of a passage home from Mallaig on 10 June 1939.
Dan McDonald Collection

Matt Sloan's *Watchful* of Maidens steaming north-west of the Heisgeir, on passage to Loch Boisdale, c 1966.
Photograph by Angus McCrindle

Andy 'Tarry' McCrindle's *Aliped IX* of Girvan at North Bay, Barra, c 1972.
Photograph by Phil McCabe, Peterhead

Neil Jackson's *Village Belle III* of Tarbert, 1967.
Photograph by Geoff Webster, Fleetwood

Battering through a head-sea in the North, Johnny McMillan's
Elma of Carradale, c 1953.
Per Alistair McMillan, Carradale

Hauling a ring-net, Moonen Bay, Skye, c 1952.
Per Denis Meenan, Campbeltown

The *Watchful* and *Wistaria* of Maidens 'squared' in Corodale
Bay, South Uist, 1960.
Per Matt Sloan, Maidens

The *Watchful* and *Saffron* of Maidens brailing herring in Loch
Carnan on a January morning, c 1965.
Photograph by Angus McCrindle

The ring-net fleet on a bustling Mallaig morning, c. 1951.
Per L Paterson

Duncan Ritchie and George McMillan.
Per L Paterson

Breakfast of fried bacon and eggs and baked beans in the
forecastle of the *Kittiwake* of Campbeltown, about 1950.
The Author's collection

Enjoying Amy McLean's ice-cream at Mallaig on a Saturday
morning, c 1935.
Per Neil Short, Glasgow

Archibald 'Baldy' Stewart at Buckingham Palace, receiving the British
Empire Medal.
Per Mrs Doreen Wareham, Campbeltown

Cover illustrations
Shooting a ring-net from the *Wistaria* of Maidens off Shepherd's Bight,
South Uist, on a summer evening, c 1967. The neighbour-boat lifting
the end of the net is the *Watchful*. Skipper Billy Sloan is in the wheelhouse of the *Wistaria* and crewmen John Watson and Tom Harvey are
on deck.
Photographs by Hugh McPhee, Dundonald

Preface

· · · · · · · · · · ·

I have to thank Edward O'Donnelly in Loch Ranza for unwittingly putting me on to this book. He asked me, in 1997, to write the text for a schools CD-ROM on the history of the Clyde herring-fishing industry, and I agreed. As part of our research for the CD-ROM project, we visited, in October of 1998, several retired fishermen in Ayrshire, and it was there that this book on the North was conceived. It had been at the back of my mind since the 1970s, but I had other writing that I wanted to do and I suppose I simply trusted that the notion would recede. I'm glad now that it didn't.

I have confined my researches on the subject to Kintyre and Ayrshire, with the exception of one source, Mr Duncan MacInnes, a native of Eriskay, who knew many of the Clyde ring-net fishermen and fished in partnership with some of them. This decision has, in part, been dictated by financial considerations, and in part by the profusion of material in the chosen area. Had I visited fishermen in Mallaig, Eriskay, Skye, Scalpay-Harris and the other areas of the Minch where a native ring-net fishery was established, this book would certainly have taken on a greater depth, but the 'North' was north only to the fishermen who operated from ports south of the Minches. To the native fishermen, the 'North' was not the north, but their home waters.

The material in this book comes from oral history and has been gathered over the period 1974 to 2000. My intention was not to write a conventional history, but to try to present the story of the North through the fishermen's memories and traditions. As originally conceived, the book was to consist almost entirely of anecdotes and tales in the dialect form in which I recorded them, but that idea was abandoned when I got to thinking that such a compilation would put off many potential readers. I have therefore rewritten the stories in English, but leaving a Scots flavour in the quotations, and in so doing have reorganised them narratively when I considered that necessary for clarity. By and large, however, I have tried to preserve the spirit of the stories.

Some informants had more to tell than others, and these individuals are well-represented, irrespective of their experience or reputation as fishermen. Everyone, however, who participated is represented, and I am grateful to all of them, not least for trusting me with their memories.

Some men were discreet in their narratives, and I'm certain there were many incidents that remained unmentioned owing to their sensitive nature. I respect that reticence, and, where informants have stated names in perhaps embarrassing circumstances, I have omitted or disguised these names. I trust, none the less, that nothing in these stories causes offence to anybody. That was never my intention.

Much of this book reflects a special fascination of mine with the relationship of ring-net fishermen with natural phenomena, in particular 'appearances' – the signs that led fishermen to herring. This is an area of knowledge that has vanished, as a practical asset, with the passing of the ring-net. It was a product of centuries of intimate observation, passed on from generation to generation, but none the less requiring, generation by generation, to be re-learned in practice. What is presented here is only the theory of seeing, hearing, smelling and feeling the presence of fish, which is quite different from the doing. I daresay these skills could be rediscovered if there were ever a need for them, which is unlikely.

The knowledge herein came from the last of the sea-going hunters, men who used their senses, in 'primitive' fashion, to detect and interpret the greatest and the smallest of indicators from the natural world. Some of them – who will be known to their peers, if to no one else who reads this book – were among the greatest of the post-war practitioners of ring-netting, perfecting their skills in the wintry waters of the Minch during the final magnificent flourish of that method. It has been my privilege to have known them and to have been their historian. Truly, in the words of the cliché, their like will never be seen again.

Acknowledgements

I have to thank all those who contributed to this compilation of stories, but in particular I thank Robert Ross, in Tarbert, both for giving me the benefit of his own knowledge and for directing me to other informants in his native village; Lachie Paterson in Carradale, for general encouragement and assistance, particularly with the assembling of photographs; Jim Munro in Troon, for organising a late flurry of telephone interviews with Ayrshire fishermen I hadn't known about; Donald J MacDonald, Harris and Ullapool, for information and advice; Iain Gemmell in Ayr for having taking the trouble to tape-record himself; Neil Short in Glasgow, Duncan Ritchie in Carradale and Duncan MacInnes in Kinlochleven, who wrote out their memories and proved themselves more than adequate for the task.

I thank all those informants who read over their own contributions and all who read the first draft of the entire work and gave me the benefit of their criticisms, namely: Tommy Ralston, Iain Gemmell, Archie Paterson, Lachie Paterson, Hugh Edgar, Matt Sloan, Robert Ross and Joe Brown. I am particularly indebted to Moira Burgess – the Campbeltown-born author – who scrutinised the first draft and provided many 'lay' criticisms which helped me produce a more generally accessible final draft. Equally, to Bob Smith in Linlithgow, who once again gave me the benefit of his acutely critical mind. Thanks also to Jim Tarvit, Anstruther, for assistance with boats' registrations, and to Bill Tudhope, Banavie, Fort William, for assistance in sourcing photographs. I thank my wife, Judy, for her guidance in computer matters, and my daughters, Sarah, Amelia and Isabella, for having done without my company while I laboured with this work. Finally, I thank all those who contributed in any way, however small. Any errors – and I've yet to write a book that was totally accurate! – are my own responsibility, but I would appreciate being told about them so that they may be corrected should the work ever be reissued.

I am indebted to Angus McCrindle in Girvan for having prepared a map of fishermen's place-names on the West Side, on which is based the map in this book. The spellings of certain of these map names may not agree with spellings found in the text. Equally, spellings within the text may vary. I am aware of these discrepancies. The only 'correct' forms are the Gaelic and Norse originals.

I have tried to establish the ownership of all photographs used in this book. If any photograph has been wrongly attributed, I apologise and will make amends in any future edition of the work.

A Geographical and Historical Introduction

The North, for the purposes of this work, may be defined broadly as two fishing areas. There was the 'West Side', which extended from Barra Head – the southernmost tip of the Outer Hebrides – to the Butt of Lewis in the north. But that long, indented coastline can itself be divided into two parts at the Sound of Harris, south of which most of the fishing effort was concentrated.

The 'West Side' was the west side of the Minch, but the east side of the Outer Hebrides. The ring-net fishermen very seldom ventured out into the Atlantic to west or south. The waters north of the Sound of Harris were considered a rather hostile area until after the Second World War, because the native and East Coast drift-net fishermen encountered there had no liking for ring-netting and were known to vent their opposition in threats and acts of violence.

On the east side of the Minch, the main fishing grounds – chiefly in summer – were around Canna, the Heisgeir and in the Skye lochs, with later forays into the Mull lochs. The main markets overall were at Mallaig, Oban and Gairloch.

Clyde herring-fishermen have gone to the Minches since the 18th century, and perhaps earlier. They went before the buss experiment in Government subsidisation of the catching and curing industry began in 1750. After the end of the buss fishery, Clyde fishermen worked the Minches in smacks. As with the buss fishery, the actual fishing was done from open boats, with the crews living in the larger boat. When the smacks were discarded in the late 19th century, and the Loch Fyne Skiff, on the Argyll side of the Firth, and the Nabby, on the Ayrshire side, became virtually the universal style of fishing craft on the Clyde, the fishermen went to the Minches in these. Some were little more than 30 feet long, but were sailed north to the winter drift-net fisheries in Loch Broom, Loch Hourn, Loch Seaforth and elsewhere.

It is arguable whether the seamanship of these skiff fishermen exceeded that of the later ring-net fishermen who ploughed the winter waters of the Minches in 50- and 60-foot motor boats, regularly crossing loaded to the mainland markets from the Outer Isles in gales of wind.

Certainly, the winter herring-fishery in the North challenged all who participated in it. Not only was weather a big factor, but also the fishing operation itself, which was often conducted in darkness along shores perilous with rocks and tide. It is remarkable – and a tribute to both boats and men – that nobody was killed and that only one boat was lost – Willie McCaffer's *Golden Gleam* of Tarbert, at the Cailleach, Mull, on 26 October 1954 – in all the years the Clyde men worked ring-nets in the North.

Essentially, these trips North were undertaken from economic necessity. When the Clyde herring-fishery was slack, the Minch fishery was always a tantalising option to the best of the crews. There were Clyde crews which never ventured to the North, having neither the mettle nor – perhaps – the boats. They remained in local waters and fished as best they could on the resources available.

By the early 20th century, the North had become the testing-ground of both boats and men. Latterly, boats were being built with North winter conditions in mind. Some crews went only for a few seasons and discovered that these conditions were not to their liking. By the mid-20th century, certain families had become regulars in the North and made a great deal of money there.

The fishermen who crewed the most successful of the boats were generally the best available, and a high proportion of them – trained to the limit – went on to become skippers and boat-owners in their own right. The most successful crews generally held together longest. A well-drilled crew, with each man knowing his tasks and able to perform them in darkness, and, moreover, alert to every difficulty and danger that might arise, itself generated success, and that success – represented by high earnings – in turn contributed to the retention of crews.

Aboard less successful boats, there was often a high turn-over in men, with the most skilled and ambitious fishermen continually seeking a berth with a high-earning team. Ring-net crews – six-strong – could also afford the luxury of employing an old man, who knew the fishing grounds and the ways of herring intimately and who could mend a net expertly, attributes that did not depend on agility and vigour. Nowadays, it would be unthinkable for a fisherman to continue working until, say, 79 years, which was the age at which Duncan McSporran of Dalintober retired.

The origins of ring-netting in the North remain obscure, but Loch Fyne fishermen working 'trawls' – the early name for small ring-nets – were the cause of trouble in Loch Hourn and Loch Nevis in 1883, when HMS *Jackal* had to be sent there to restore order; and again in 1884, when the Fishery Board stationed a cutter on the fishing grounds for the

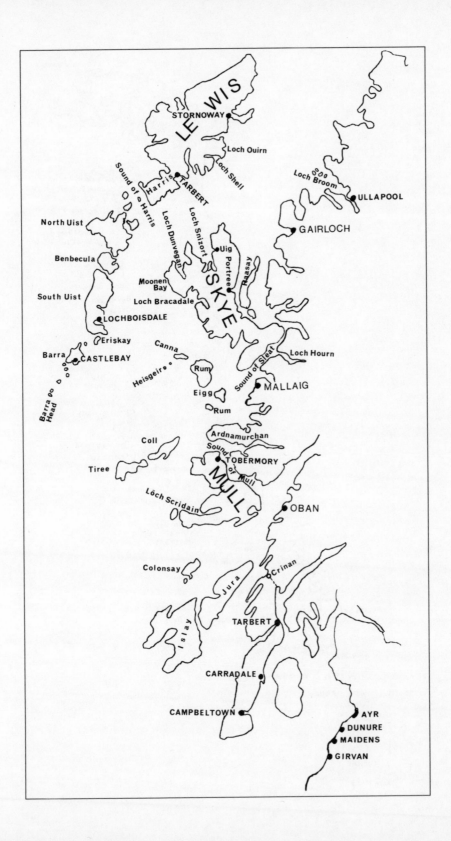

Loch Uskavagh

South Fords

WIAY

Loch Carnan

Davie's Hole
Loch Skiport
The Duff
Shepherd's Bight
Usinish
Cleft Rock Bay
The Cleft Rock

Kettle

SOUTH UIST

Corodale

Moonlight Bay

Bay Bolum
Loch Eynort
Billy's Bight

Stuleys

Deer Island

Tarry's Bight
Loch Boisdale

Lochboisdale

Dalliburgh

Calvay
nord Bay
Bagh Harty

Sound of Eriskay

Calvay Bight

Melvaig Head

ERISKAY

politician

Duke's Rock
Hartamul

Gull Rock

Weaver's Castle

Barra Sound

FUDAY

GIGHAY

Seal Bay
Kruger's Bight
HELLISAY

Northbay

BARRA

Curachan

Castlebay

Brevig
Blower
Telephone Bay

VATERSAY

Fairway

Bobby Shaun Buoy

MULDOANICH

Sandray Sound

SANDRAY

Wine Glass

Pabbay Sound

PABBAY

MINGULAY

BERNERAY

Barra Head

trawlers' protection from native drift-net fishermen. In 1885, the cutter *Daisy* had to be sent to Loch Eil to protect the Loch Fyne trawl-fishermen.[1]

1915 or thereabouts seems the likely period in which the method began to be used openly by Campbeltown boats in Loch Bracadale, Skye (p 8). There were sporadic earlier uses, but these must have been of a furtive character. In time, however, many of the native fishermen – from Skye, Wester Ross, Scalpay-Harris and Eriskay notably – seeing the success of the Clyde men on their very doorsteps, adopted ring-netting and themselves became adept at the job. Of the indigenous ring-netting families, the Mansons of Mallaig and MacKinnons of Eriskay were perhaps the most prominent.

Ring-net crews also came to the Minch from the East Coast of Scotland, where, however, the method never took hold outside of the relatively sheltered waters of the Moray Firth and Firth of Forth. In 1933, an attempt at ring-netting off the Aberdeenshire coast was made by a crew from Girvan, in conjunction with a (presumably apprentice) crew from Boddam, but the effort was abandoned after two weeks, owing largely to the swell in the open waters proving 'too great'.[2] Among the most prominent of the East Coast boats in the Minch, during the post-war period, may be mentioned the *Falcon, Flourish, Rosehaugh* and *Aspire* from the Moray Firth and the *Stardust, Achates, Hope, Good Design, Guiding Light* and *Minnie Wood* from the South Firth of Forth.[3]

After the Second World War, there was a Manx presence – albeit slight – in the North. At least the *Manx Rose* and *Manx Lily*, part-crewed by Campbeltown fishermen, are known to have operated there. There was even a pair of ringers – the *Provider* and *Success* – appeared from Whitby, on the Yorkshire coast, one year in the 1950s. They swept up alongside a pair of Manson boats on the West Side and the first question one of the English skippers asked was: 'Where the fuck are we?' They had got there without so much as a chart between them![4]

A brief account of the operation of ring-netting will be necessary if the more technical elements are to be grasped. Those readers who desire a deeper understanding of the method, I would direct to my *The Ring-Net Fishermen*. Ring-netting was essentially a two-boat operation, so skippers would pair off and take a neighbour, or 'neebor'. Some partnerships endured for decades, others for mere months. The crew that located a shoal, or 'spot', of herring would set, or 'shot', its net. The end of the net would then be picked up by the neighbouring crew and towed around to meet the net-boat. A circle, or 'ring', was thus formed, hence the description ring-netting. The boats would then meet to close the ring, and the neighbouring crew would transfer aboard the net-boat to help haul in the net; and while the net was being hauled, the other boat would keep a strain on the net-boat, by means of a connecting rope, to prevent that boat from being pulled over the net and to preserve the shape of the net. Once the bottom, or 'sole', of the net had been closed, the herring were trapped. When the net-hauling had been completed, only the bag, or 'top sling', would remain, containing the catch, which would then be 'dried up' alongside. The towing-boat would then cast off and come round to 'square' the boats by also lashing on to the bag on its opposite side. With the net secure between the two boats, the removal of the catch from the net could begin, using a winch-operated bag-net called the 'brailer'.

The traditional drift-net, which also features in this account, was a more passive method of fishing, consisting of a string, or 'train', of connected nets suspended from the surface. Nets and boats drifted together through the night and, if herring were swimming, the fish might strike into the meshes and be enmeshed.

These accounts, in the words of the Clyde ring-net fishermen, tell part of the story of the conquest of the North. There is no doubt much more that could have been told, but had these vestiges not been gathered now, in even 10 years' time little would have remained.

The North fishing was perhaps the last great collective adventure that the Clyde fishermen enjoyed. There are now no herring-boats left on the Clyde, and the fishing communities there – complex with layers of interrelationships, extending back centuries, and each with its own char- acteristics – are dwindling as economic decline and rampant bureaucracy take their toll. Such harbours as Dunure and Maidens are silted up and devoid of fishing craft. The end that has come upon the once prosperous and innovative Clyde herring-fishing communities has been as sudden as it has been tragic.

Early Ventures
·······················

With drift-nets

Hugh MacFarlane's earliest experiences of the North were as a drift-net fisherman in an old skiff, the *Mary* of Tarbert. The crew of four would set sail for Loch Broom in October, after the 'traalin', or ring-netting, was finished in Loch Fyne, and would always try to be home for New Year. The boat was 33ft (10.06m) long and 9ft (2.74m) of beam with a tiny forecastle in which the men could 'have a doss an cook a meal … that's aboot all'. There were few lights on the coast at that time, and he remembered the lighthouse at Rudha Reidh, south of Loch Broom, being built. (It was completed in 1912.) He also fished with drift-nets in Loch Hourn and Loch Nevis and in Loch Eishort, where, he recalled, 'ye winna get a shillin a basket'. [Hugh MacFarlane]

The native fishermen were universally opposed to ring-netting, which they believed drove the herring shoals off the coast. Such was the prevailing hostility that the Tarbertmen were often suspected of landing ring-net herring when, in actuality, the herring had been caught in drift-nets. Hugh MacFarlane attributed the misconception to the Tarbertmen's approach to drift-netting. In a sense, they brought the science of ring-netting to the practice of drift-netting. The Tarbertmen – and no doubt others among the Kintyre fishermen – weren't shooting their drift-nets until they would locate herring, whereas the native drift-netters would 'go oot an throw the nets away anywhere'. The Tarbertmen would be in along the land, perhaps where the natives weren't seeing them, and would set their nets to trap the herring on the shore, at times having to 'fend off wi an oar'. Consequently, as Hugh MacFarlane put it: 'We wir gettin too many herrin for their idea, wi the drift-nets.'

At the back of Horse Island

As an example of that success, he told of one 'dark as dye' October night in Loch Broom with the *Mary*, when herring were heard 'playin dry in along the rocks' at the back of Horse Island. The crew shot eight 'barrels' of drift-nets along the shore, but not content with that, they later went off in the skiff's tiny dinghy and secured each end of the train to the very shore so that the herring couldn't 'get away oot by the en'. Still not satisfied, the crew then set four spare nets inside the first train. Periodically, they'd lift one of the net-buoys and check if the fish were beginning to 'make', and the indications were good, prompting Hugh to predict: 'If that'll cerry along the train, ye'll fill the skift in the moarnin'. Then the herring began jumping in such numbers that Hugh's brother John was able to catch them in his hands. With daylight, the herring began leaving the shore – as herring must – and swam straight into the walls of netting. As the *Mary*, fully loaded, headed for market under oars, she passed a native boat by the name of the *Brothers Pride*, whose crew was hauling barren nets out in the tide-stream. 'Where did you get the herring?' one of the native crew called. 'We got them right inside o where ye are,' a Tarbertmen replied. The doleful answer to that was: 'Well, well, what a pity and us so near.' [Hugh MacFarlane]

With ring-nets from Campbeltown

The development of ring-netting in the North was a tentative and gradual process, which has been documented in this author's book, The Ring-Net Fishermen.

Duncan McSporran believed that 'the first man tae go up tae the North wi a ring-net' was Robert Robertson, known as the 'Hoodie'. In about 1914, at a time when fishing was slack in home waters, Robertson put drift-nets aboard his skiff the *Brothers*, but also concealed, in the sternsheets, 'a wee ring-net' which he used 'on the quiet', the idea being to go out at night and pretend he was working drift-nets, and if he 'got intae a good eye o herrin', to produce the ring-net and use that. The next time he went North, he 'jeest went quite openly wi the ring-net'. Duncan Blair reckoned that Robert Robertson first went to Loch Bracadale with a ring-net in 1916.

The first ring-nets that Hugh MacFarlane was aware of in the North were used beyond Loch Broom, 'away ootside clear o everybody', in about 1912. The boats involved were all from Campbeltown: Neil McLean and company's *May Queen* and *Harvest Queen* and Archie and Denis McKay's *Noel* and *Annunciata*. The ring-nets were concealed below the boats' sternsheets and the Tarbert fishermen knew they were in use, but wouldn't say. Nor did the Campbeltown crews wish the Tarbertmen to know what they were up to. They would be shooting their drift-nets, and, as the Campbeltown boats passed by, would shout: 'Where are ye goin?' – 'We're away for home!' one of the Campbeltown crews would reply. But they'd return soon afterwards, loaded with herring, and discharge them in Loch Broom as though they'd been taken in drift-nets.

Donald McIntosh maintained that Dugald Blair of Campbeltown 'opened up the Minch' to ring-netting, along with his brother Archie, who together fished the *Maggie McNab* and *Glad Tidings*. Dugald Blair was drift-netting one year in Loch Bracadale, Skye, and had been there several weeks when he heard that his brother was going North too with drift-nets. He wrote and told him to take a ring-net with him, a message which Archie relayed to Dugald's wife, Maggie, saying: 'Well, A've got a letter fae him here an he waants me tae take up a ring-net. Does he waant tae get me shot?' [Duncan Blair]

That anecdote belongs, obviously, to a period – probably the years immediately prior to the outbreak of the First World War – when ring-netting was still a taboo subject in most parts of the Hebrides; but it also implies that the Kintyre fishermen's acquiescence in the matter was under strain. By that time, fishermen who depended on ring-netting as the primary source of their income had come to resent the high cost and relatively low yield of drift-nets, which increasingly they considered both inefficient and obsolescent. It was only a matter of time before they rebelled against the unlawful restrictions placed upon them and began to use ring-nets, albeit cautiously at first, on the fishing grounds of the North. By the 1920s, the ring-net was a fixture in the Minch, despite the continued hostility of those fishermen – native and East Coast alike – who adhered to the traditional method and who formed, by far, the majority.

With ring-nets from Ayrshire

The first Ayrshire ring-netters to venture North, by Turner McCrindle's recollection, were the Maidens boats *Golden West* (John and Thomas McCrindle), *Margarita* and *Twin Sisters* (both belonging to Thomas Sloan and brothers) and the *Aurora* of Girvan (James McCreath).

James McCreath, however, believed that his first trip North, in 1929, was with the first *May* (launched in that year), partnering the Gemmell brothers' *Mary Sturgeon* of Dunure. They fished first around Canna and then crossed to the Skye shore and worked their way around the north of the island.

Turner McCrindle recalled that the buyer, Davie Woods, was North in a herring-steamer – the *Recruit* he believed – which the Ayrshire boats filled once at Soay. They fished about Canna generally and around Soay and in Loch Pooltiel, but when the wind would change to easterly or south-easterly, the boats would cross the Minch to the West Side. When, however, the wind would shift again, into the west, they would finish with the West Side and head back across the Minch. These movements, backwards and forwards, followed the wind-driven drift of the plankton, which concentrated on lee shores and brought feeding herring with it. In July, the crews generally left the North, because the fishing began to slacken, and the Isle of Man became their base.

Matt Sloan was certain that the Ayrshire ringers went to the summer fishing in the North before they went to the winter fishing. He remembered that, when a schoolboy, the *Golden West*, the first *Margarita*, and the *Aurora* and *Twin Sisters*, which were both older boats of the traditional Ayrshire 'nabby' build, were away at the summer fishing in the Minch, mostly about Soay and up as far as Loch Bracadale. When the boxing of herring started in the Minch summer fishery (p 80), these older boats were simply too small to carry sufficient boxes.

Opening up the West Side

Matt Sloan thought it probable that the West Side – from the Sound of Harris to Barra Head, more or less – was opened up to ring-netting by the Mansons of Mallaig. The Mallaig men, he believed, spent their winters, in the early years, largely about Loch Bracadale, before venturing across the Minch and starting a fishery there. Tommy Ralston, however, was told that the Blairs of Campbeltown were the first ring-net fishermen on the West Side.

> *A petition of the Sea League, which was formed in 1933 (p 129), referred to ring-net boats in Loch Eynort, South Uist, in the winter of 1927-28, and accused the ring-net fishermen of having 'dumped so many herrings that the whole place was polluted with putrid fish so that the people could not come out of their houses owing to the smell of decaying herrings',[5] but there is no indication of where these boats came from.*
>
> *The West Side, however, was hardly virgin ground for herring fishermen. Native drift-net fishermen had been active there for generations; drift-net crews from the Clyde had been exploiting the Minches as a whole since at least the early 18th century, and drifters from the East Coast of Scotland were certainly operating in the lochs and inlets of the West Side before ring-netting was ever introduced there.*

Anchored drift-nets

'Rice' Reid, an East Coast fisherman who had begun his working life on drift-netters and who later switched to ring-netting from Girvan with 'Tarry' McCrindle, used to talk of being in Loch Eynort, South Uist, in a steam-drifter, working anchored drifts. 'They were workin these anchored nets up in an area o Loch Eynort which we were never in,' Matt Sloan commented. They carried so many drift-nets in a dinghy up through the narrow channel at the head of the loch and were catching herring in the upper reaches while the drifter lay at anchor in the main loch. That practice of setting drift-nets to anchors in confined sea-areas was not an uncommon one. Neil Short, for example, recollected going into the Kettle Drum – an inlet of Loch Skiport – one morning in the winter of 1938 and seeing a steam-drifter inside the anchorage. The crew was hauling anchored nets and took 80 crans of herring from them.

As long as the Clyde fishermen confined their activities to drift-netting when in the North, they were tolerated by both native and East Coast fishermen, but whenever they began working the ring-net, surreptitiously or otherwise, conflict inevitably arose. On virtually all the fishing grounds to which the ring-net was taken, the method was resisted: in upper Loch Fyne in the mid-19th century; at Donegal, Islay and the Ballantrae Banks in the late 19th century; in the Firth of Forth in the late 1920s. The North was no different. Drift-net fishermen there, as elsewhere, were thoroughly outfished and resented the fact.

In 1933, an investigation into the West Coast fisheries was undertaken by the Fishery Board for Scotland, and its findings among crofter-fishermen included complaints that ring-netting broke up and scattered the shoals and wastefully destroyed great quantities of immature herring. There were, between the wars, native ring-net fishermen operating from Skye and the Mainland, but it wasn't until the fishermen of the Outer Isles, after the Second World War, seriously adopted ring-netting, that the method became acceptable on these coasts. The following accounts will demonstrate the nature of that conflict between tradition and innovation.

If the intimidation in the story which follows seems improbable, consider the wrecking of two Tarbert skiffs by East Coast drift-net boats at Ullapool on 28 Dec 1908, as recorded in the Fishery Board for Scotland's Annual Report. The Evening Star *(TT 80) was 'damaged and sunk at her moorings' by the* Chrysolite *(INS 183) while the* Alma Lloyd *(TT 238) was 'driven from her anchor and wrecked on the beach' by the* Treasure *(INS 540).*

'It wouldn't be so good for your throat'

When Hugh MacFarlane first went to the North, the Tarbertmen wouldn't dare mention a ring-net, let alone produce one. They would set out in October for Loch Broom, fish there – with drift-nets – until Christmas and then return home. One winter, around 1910, Hugh and an older brother, Neil, landed on the beach at Ullapool below the Royal Hotel. They were in for a cask of water and this 'North Heilanman' appeared on the beach. 'A doot,' he said, 'you've a trawl.' – 'Oh, no,' Neil replied, 'we've no trawl. It's all the same as yersel.' Hugh was in the dinghy, lifting aboard the water-cask, and turned to the native, who was enormously-built, 'a monster': 'What aboot it if we had?' To this challenge, the native replied with an undisguised threat: 'It wouldn't be so good for yer trot [throat].' Hugh's brother turned to him with the warning: 'You shut up yer mooth now.' Hugh later conceded: 'A wis only young; A dinna know.' [Hugh MacFarlane]

Refusal to gut ring-net herring

The fishing community on Scalpay-Harris resisted ring-netting until after the Second World War. Ironically, that same community was the last stronghold of the method. Its involvement in ring-netting spanned the period 1946-1974. As D J MacDonald observed, in the summer of 2000: 'Only two boats over 50ft remain of the once-envied Scalpay fleet'.

When a Tarbert crew went into Scalpay-Harris – between the wars – to sell a catch of herring, the salesman there – who was from Kyle of Lochalsh – said to the fishermen, 'You'll get the price that's going. Dump them in there.' Hugh MacFarlane said to him: 'What's wrong?' The salesman's reply was: 'If you're goin to stay here the night, you'll need to anchor out in the middle there.' – 'What for?' Hugh asked, puzzled. 'They're up in arms against the trawled herring. The women's refusing to gut the herring.' When Hugh looked about him, the women were standing silently in 'wee bunches'. As soon as the catch was sold – merely 60 baskets from Loch Snizort – the fishermen filled fuel and started the engine. No one had spoken to them. The salesman returned and warned them again: 'You'll not be safe. If you're going to stay here, you'll not dare go ashore.' The Tarbert crew decided to choose the safer option, and started back immediately for Loch Snizort. [Hugh MacFarlane]

Hostility from Stornoway fishermen

North of Loch Maddy was a 'no-go' area for ring-netters in the 1930s. Jock McIntyre recalled that, in Loch Eport, North Uist – the furthest the Campbeltown crews ventured during that period – the Stornoway small-boat drifters would scowl and glower and shake their fists at the ring-net men at work in daylight.

Rejecting ring-net herring

One morning in the winter of 1946, Davie McNaughton was in Tarbert-Harris with the *Nobles*. They had no herring, but a Girvan pair, the *Carrick Lass* and *Avail*, came in with 100 cran, sold through Stornoway. About 50 cran – 200 boxes – had been loaded on to the SS *Dunara Castle* when those handling the catch discovered that it was ring-net herring. 'Every damnt herrin wis put back on the quay!' [David McNaughton]

Shot at in Loch Shell

The first time the *Storm Drift* and *Summer Rose*, in company with the *Hope* and *Good Design*, ventured into Loch Shell, on the south-east coast of Lewis, one of the 'Heilanmen' fired off a rifle in their direction. There was no intent to cause injury, the fishermen believed – it was a warning-shot, to persuade the ringers to get out of a drift-netting preserve. That was in the winter of 1948. [Grieve Gemmell]

Fasteners

When the *Lily* of Campbeltown and the *Fionnaghal* of Tarbert went into Camus Tianavaig, south of Portree, one morning, there was a massive play of herring in the centre of the bay. As the *Lily*'s crew prepared to shoot the net, the neighbour-boat 'cut them oot' – shot ahead of them. 'Ye never saw such a mess o a net in yer life,' Davie McNaughton recalled. Into the middle of the bay, drift-net fishermen – presumed to be from Portree – had dumped scrapped motor cars, old engines, rusted ploughs, and much else of the sort, as a deterrent to ring-net fishermen. The *Fionnaghal*'s net had snagged on the scrap and was so severely damaged that the crews didn't have it completely mended until about a fortnight later. There was a fleet of small open drift-netters in the bay that morning, but these boats were all on the margins. When the crews went into Portree with the bad net, a local man, Davie Sinclair, explained that the scrap had been dumped to repel the Skye ring-netters that fished out of Broadford. [David McNaughton]

At odds

Joe Brown of Campbeltown admitted that, even post-1945, the ringers and drifters 'never got on', the two methods being so different. The drift-netters – sometimes 30 or more in an area – each lay to miles of nets, and ringers working among those fleets of nets might locate herring, yet refrain from shooting their own nets for fear of becoming entangled with the drifts. Generally, the ringers tried to avoid the areas the drifters were fishing, but disputes did occur, and some ring-net fishermen would burst drift-net buoys with the skiddoag or boat-hook, so that the drift-nets would sink away and allow the ringers room to shoot their own net. The drift-netters – mostly from the East Coast – were known to provoke the ring-net men when both sets of boats would meet to land their catches in such ports as Mallaig. The drifter skippers would put their bigger boats' heads into the quay, leave the engine in gear and churn away until the ringers had been shoved to the side. Then there would be rows – 'bechs an roars an shouts'. [Joe Brown]

'The men that stabbed me faither's buies'

Robert McGown conceded that the bursting of drift-net buoys went on in Loch Striven, on the Clyde, when drifters and ringers worked together, between the wars, in these confined waters, and he heard East Coast herring girls shout at ring-net fishermen going into Mallaig with a catch: 'There's the men that stabbed me faither's buies!' [Robert McGown]

Ruined

Archie Paterson spoke one day to an old Skyeman in Portnalong, and the man said to him: 'The ringers ruined the herring fishing. All these lochs were filled with herring.' [Archibald Paterson]

Impressions
. . . .

The North meant many things to the men who fished there. Some enjoyed it; some didn't. Some hardly wanted to leave it; others couldn't leave it quick enough. Some went occasionally; others went every year. A few were never there at all. In Dunure, those crews who kept out of the North were known derisively as 'the

Home Patrol'. A large proportion of the Carradale crews, for example, had no liking for the North and went there only out of necessity.

There were several reasons why the North fishing, and in particular the winter fishing, was so disliked. For a start, few individuals whose home lives are comfortable and secure leave home for lengthy periods without experiencing, at the very least, regret. The average fisherman missed his wife and children or his girlfriend as much as the next man, and perhaps more so given that his work took him nightly not only from home, but from land itself.

The prospect of being away from home for up to six weeks or more was too much for some fishermen – skippers included – to stomach. By remaining in local waters, a crew stood to lose out in earnings; then again, trips North were more expensive in provisions and fuel, and some trips ended in failure and debt. Although, as a rule, herring were more abundant in the North and easier fished, there was the run across the Minch to market to contend with, and in winter conditions that passage could be daunting, even for the best of boats with the best of crews. Finally, crews were often storm-bound for days and even weeks at a time in the winter and the sheer tedium of prolonged confinement aboard a small boat did nothing for morale.

There were men who actually enjoyed absences from home. Some of them simply preferred the company of fellow-fishermen, especially when drink was flowing and they were free to indulge without fear of falling foul of wife or girl-friend. Others enjoyed extra-marital relations with women in ports they visited, particularly the holiday resorts of the Yorkshire coast and Isle of Man during the summer fishings there in the 1950s; but if such liaisons blossomed in the wintry outposts of the Hebrides, there is no knowledge of them, and the proba-bility is slight, to say the least.

Ultimately, however, what drew ring-net crews to the North – and all other distant fisheries – was the prospect of big money; and fortunes were certainly made in the North. The most ambitious skippers were not content to linger in the Clyde when the herring fishing there slackened. They wanted to be among herring and filling their boats night after night, accumulating capital and investing it in bigger and better boats and in the latest navigational and fish-finding equipment that technology could offer. They were driven by a hunger for success, and the North drew them, season after season, like bees to a honey-pot.

Palm trees

Archie Paterson, whose *Harvest Queen* was perhaps the most regular in the North of the Carradale post-war fleet, stated, 'We went tae the North when we had tae go', adding that 'some o the boys wirna very keen tae go'.

One Carradale skipper famously remarked, after a maddeningly long spell storm-bound, 'There will be palm-trees growin in Lochboisdale before I come back!' [James Macdonald]

Magneto over the side

A Campbeltown fisherman reputedly removed the magneto from the engine of the boat he was crewing on and flung it over the side to delay a trip to the Minch, a misdemeanour of which he was reminded one day when an intoxicated fellow-fisherman saw him bowling at Argyll Bowling Green and shouted to him over the wall: 'They tell me, cousin, that you threw the magneto over the side, but I don't believe them!' [Neil McDougall]

'... On the way to Hell'

Some Campbeltown ringers were passing through the Crinan Canal one year on their way to the North winter fishing. A doomsday advocate of an obscure religious sect, holding an umbrella with pessimistic warnings stuck all over it, called to the fishermen: 'You're on the way to Hell!' One fisherman shouted back, 'Ye might have somethin there!', while Baldy Stewart blew a raspberry. [Iain Johnston, Campbeltown, 1977]

Farewell

When Hugh Edgar was in his first winter in the Minch, as boy in the *Hercules*, they left the mouth of Loch Boisdale knowing that they were going home; it was about the end of January and the fishing was finished. As the coastline of South Uist began to recede, an older crewman, Jock Dunlop, looked out the wheelhouse door and intoned: 'Farewell, ye hills o misery ...' [Hugh Edgar]

Motivation

To the question of what motivated the Clyde fishermen to spend a large part of their working year in the Minch, there is one certain answer – economic need. Even before the ring-net was taken to the Hebrides, the Clyde fishermen were going there with drift-nets, and for the same reason. Hugh MacFarlane of Tarbert put it this way: 'There wir no help in any way. Ye had tae make it or ye widn't have it. That's what wis puttin us away tae the North.' When the herring left Loch Fyne around

October, that's when the Tarbert fishermen, and their counterparts farther up the loch, got ready to sail north.

'The prize wis big'

Peter McDougall of Tarbert remarked, 'If ye dinna go tae the North ye hanna a year's earnins – it wis as simple as that', and Neil Jackson added: 'It wis eether that or ten rings in Loch Striven for a hunder baskets – no way!' Loch Striven is one of the Clyde sea-lochs and 'ten rings' meant 10 arduous hauls of the net in one night, and for a paltry yield. In the North, one ring of the net often filled a pair of boats, and sometimes two and three pairs of boats. That was the difference. As Robert Ross put it: 'The prize wis big, ye know; the prize wis big in the North. When ye got herrin, ye got a lot. It wisna a wee puckle o baskets ye got. If ye got fifty or sixty baskets, as a rule they wir ran away. Aye, ye could make a livin in the Clyde, but ye could make a big livin in the North for a lot less labour.' The Ayrshire fishermen felt exactly the same. 'We depended on the North, the months in the North, tae make wir year up,' Willie Anderson remarked.

'Liftin the boat oot the watter'

The legendary abundance of herring in the North finds expression in the following anecdote. Jim Munro was standing alongside the *Britannia*'s wheelhouse one night at the mouth of Loch Boisdale and overheard a skipper talking over the radio to Andy 'Tarry' McCrindle of the *Aliped IX*. 'Are ye seein anythin, Andy?' he enquired of the Girvan skipper. 'Aye,' 'Tarry' replied. 'Herrin? They're liftin the boat oot the watter here!' [Jim Munro]

The 'Toms'

The nickname 'Tom' appears to have been given to Donald McDougall, father of the brothers named below, on account of his frequent use of the Gaelic word tom, *which described a lump of herring playing or in the burning.*

From 25 April 1949 to 12 December 1952, Robert Ross crewed on the *Mairearad* of Tarbert, whose skipper was Archie McDougall. Her 'neebor', or partner, was the *Fionnaghal*, skippered by Donald McDougall and with Peter McDougall as a crew-member. These McDougalls were collectively known as the 'Toms'. Together with the Jacksons, they formed the elite of the Tarbert families that fished the North. They were not only regulars in the Minch, but 'loved it up there', according to Robert Ross, and 'wid've made that thir base'. Week-ends home were infrequent and tended to be brief. Robert recalled getting back to Tarbert by bus from Crinan one Saturday night and leaving home again at two o'clock on the Sunday afternoon. He had a bath, a change of clothes and 'away straight back again'. 'The fleet wid be in Boisdale – we'd be lyin up at the quay in Skiport lookin at the heather an goats. Ye wid discherge on a Seterday in Mallaig an ye'd leave on the Seterday night, go back tae Canna, drap the anchor in Canna or go alongside the quay in Canna an go away across on Sunday. Ye dinna spend any money!' [Robert Ross]

Jim Munro has never forgotten his initial impression of the Outer Hebrides, arriving there on his first trip from Dunure in the *Britannia*. He remembered 'steamin up along the shore an thinkin about how bare the land wis wi lack o trees an vegetation', compared with the green southern coasts. For those fishermen who enjoyed being in the North, the beauty and remoteness of the islands around which they fished were impressions which never faded. Iain Gemmell of Dunure recalled one lovely calm evening when, in the *New Dawn*, they steamed for an hour into the south-west from Barra Head, 'a most exhilarating experience, knowing that there was nothing between [us] and Nantucket Lighthouse in America'.

Trips Remembered

Duncan Blair

Duncan Blair's 'first go at the North' at ring-netting was in 1920, when four pairs of Campbeltown boats went to Canna: the Blairs' own pair, Robert Robertson's pair, *Sweet Home* and *Frigate Bird*, Archie Mathieson's *Perseverance* and Duncan Wilkinson's *Ellen*, and the *Lady Charlotte* and *Lady Edith*, skippered by Neil MacKenzie and James Robertson, respectively. They fished around Rum and Canna, often finishing out at the Heisgeir, a group of lit rocks five miles south-west of Canna.

In 1928, the year that the *Bengullion* was launched, the Blair boats were late in starting North and actually met other Campbeltown ringers in the Crinan Canal, but these crews were heading back and assured the Blairs: 'Ye nee'na go up thonder – it's feenished.' The advice was disregarded and the Blairs carried on and fished Harris and around the Ascrib Islands, running the herring to Tarbert-Harris. The crews returned from an eight- or 10-week trip with a wage of £50 a man, which, as Duncan Blair remarked, 'wis something then'.

1929 was a hopeless year in the Clyde. The Blairs tried Loch Indaal, Islay (where a herring fishery had boomed in the late 19th century) and netted 20-odd cran, which were sold at Oban after a 13-hour run from Islay. They returned to Loch Indaal, but were disappointed – '… there wirna a herrin tae be seen or felt or heard …' – and went home, just in time to see Robert Robertson's crews setting out for Tiree. These crews' first landing from the Tiree grounds was 100 cran. When the Blairs heard of this, they 'upped stick an away for Tiree' but, as it turned out, there were no more herring landed from Tiree that year and at the mouth of Tobermory harbour they met Robertson's crews returning from Tiree with the news that, 'Sloan has landed a big fishin – five hunner baskets fae the mooth o the Clyde – ye better come away hame'.

Their minds, however, had already been made up. They were waiting in the North. Duncan Blair had been in the Post Office in Tobermory, wiring home for money to refuel and stock up with provisions for another look at Tiree, and got speaking to the postmistress. She told him that she had a letter from her brother, an Exciseman by the name of MacColl, who was in Lochboisdale and had reported good prospects of a fishery beginning there when the Klondykers arrived. Duncan was sceptical and told the woman that that had been the story with them all year, going here and going there and the herring ever elusive. 'There's plenty of signs of herring,' the woman insisted, 'but they're waiting for a market.'

The Blairs duly headed across to the West Side and the first shot they had was in the South Fords of Benbecula – 'a wile place tae be workin … rocks, shoals, you name it an it wis there' – 90 or 100 cran, which was divided between the two boats and landed in Mallaig. As soon as the local ring-net crews – Mansons and all – saw boats in with herring, they came down to the quay, established where the herring had been taken and then wasted no time in getting across the Minch. In fact, they set off while the Blairs' herring was still being discharged, having first booked a drifter to run their fish to Mallaig.

By the time the Blairs got under way to head back across, the wind was freshening to a gale and they had to run to Canna. They were confined there for almost a week with weather. When at last they got back to the fishing grounds, they too hired a drifter to take their catches to market. The conditions were that a half of the earnings went to the drifter and the other half to the ring-netters, but that arrangement allowed both boats to remain constantly on the fishing grounds, and the Blairs returned from that trip with a reasonable 'divide'.

Jock McIntyre

Jock McIntyre joined Robert Robertson's consortium on 17 October 1930, as a crewman on the *Kestrel*. His first trip was to Tiree, but the boats got caught there with a fortnight of bad weather and couldn't get out, though the crews were seeing herring swimming 'in red lumps' outside Scarinish harbour. A fine morning came and they were able to leave, but the herring had also left, so they carried on and landed in Loch Skiport. A gale blew that first night there, but the following morning they netted 400 cran in Loch Carnan. The drifter they had engaged to run their catches to Mallaig, the *Rose Valley*, hadn't yet arrived, so the *Kestrel* took about 150 cran, the *Kittiwake* 100 cran and John Short's *Nil Desperandum* the remainder, and ran them to Mallaig. Thereafter, the *Rose Valley* ran the herring and the four boats fished, following the herring northwards to Loch Maddy, which was as far as the crews would go at that time, owing to the hostility of the Stornoway drift-net fishermen. That fishery lasted about seven weeks, during which period the four boats killed 1680 cran of herring at an average of 30s a cran: 10s to each pair of boats and 10s to the carrier. On the day before Christmas Eve, they left Loch Boisdale and headed home, taking the outside of Islay and not stopping until they reached Campbeltown 23 hours 30 minutes later.

Neil Short

'My first trip to the North was in April 1933. The first thing was to stock up with stores as unless you were in Mallaig there was nothing to be had. We took flour, tins of meat, dried fruit, etc. We were in company that day – a Sunday – with the *Felicia*, *Faustina*, *Falcon* and the *Frigate Bird*. After about nine hours we arrived in Crinan where we tied up rather than bore the tide through the Sound of Mull. We eventually got under way and went into Tobermory to fill the fuel tank. It was the early days of diesel engines and there was no diesel fuel, only paraffin. We took some aboard, which kept us going until we got to Mallaig in a week's time.

'My memory of that fishing is that it wasn't very successful. We seemed to be all over the place – Canna, the Skye lochs, the north end of Skye, into Portree. We went over to Boisdale from Canna and thought we saw a Loch Fyne skiff. My Father went to look and found it was a skiff that had belonged to Campbeltown – John 'Plimsoll' McLellan's *Catherine and Agnes* – and been sold to Eriskay. The rest of that week was spent out in the Boisdale area, but fishing was slack and by Friday evening we had decided to go to Mallaig for the week-end. Mallaig was like a frontier town and you could only get the basics there. After seven weeks we decided to go home and clean the barnacles from the boats' bottoms. The two boats were put on the beach and the barnacles were very thick. We had to get Dutch hoes to scrape them off. No sooner had we finished than word came of some better shots, so we went again.

'This second time we were away four weeks, so you can imagine for a boy of about 16 it was quite an experience. The divide was about £20 for about 11 weeks. The first time we went into Pooltiel and looked ashore, it was all thatched houses. The township where all the old houses were is known as Glendale. I passed through there some years ago and it is very much changed – all modern houses and not a thatched one in sight.

'The following year – '34 – we got some reasonable shots around the Heisgeir. On the way out, one evening, the engine started vibrating madly. When we slowed the engine and put it in neutral it appeared all right. One of the men looked over the stern and saw that one blade had come off the propeller – we only had two blades. The neighbour-boat towed us to Mallaig and my Father had to go to Glasgow for a new propeller.

'The next season – '35 – turned out disappointing. The engine in the *Nulli Secundus* suffered severe damage. We had landed a good shot in Mallaig and had just arrived back in Canna when we broke down and had to return to Mallaig, where the engine was completely dismantled and sent to the Gleniffer works in Glasgow in a railway truck. It was fully five weeks before the boat was out again and fishing. In the meantime, our neighbour, the *Nil Desperandum*, teamed up with another boat, the *May* from Girvan, whose neighbour-boat had suffered engine trouble at the same time. The two boats fished very well together, but on the whole it was a disastrous season for us.

'The four seasons that I fished in the *Nulli Secundus* in the North all followed the same pattern. The '37 fishing was a failure and I wasn't in the North that year. That was the year the *Nulli Secundus* and the *Nil Desperandum* were sold. In '38 and '39 I fished the North in the *King Fisher*. Herring were more plentiful and these were more successful years. Some good shots in the Canna ground and the Boisdale area. The Boisdale ground stretched from Loch Skiport in the north to the Curachan in the south, and on down as far as Vatersay.'

Denis Meenan

Denis Meenan's first trip to the North was in 1941 with the *Gratitude*. That was a summer fishing around Canna and the Heisgeir and in Moonen Bay. Herring were mostly located through the presence of hunting gannets and of 'feeding', reddish lumps of plankton which the swirl of tides would carry into the shore and on which herring fed. He didn't go to the winter fishing in the North until after he came back from the Navy in 1948.

Cecil Finn

On Cecil Finn's first trip to the North summer fishing in the *Stella Maris*, as a boy of 15, they struck in just north of the Wine Gless on Vatersay, and took 150 cran of herring from one ring in the afternoon. One of the crew, old Neilly McLean, summoned Cecil, who was fending off the boats. 'Come on an see this, son,' he said, 'because ye'll probably never see this in yer life again.' The herring were exceptionally large – about 100 to the basket – and of the finest quality. 'Ye don't get herrin that size on the West Side noo,' Cecil remarked. 'Beautiful herrin they wir. An that wis in the efternoon, among red feedin an sail-fish.'

Matt Sloan

The echo-sounder – encountered here for the first time – is an electronic device which records the depth and nature of the seabed and detects shoals of fish. Although briefly experimented with in the 1930s, on the Nobles *of Campbeltown and the* Golden Sheaf *of Maidens, it did not become standard equipment on ring-netters until c 1950, the Kelvin-Hughes 'MS 24' being the first popular model. Thereafter, the instrument became indispensable, and during the fishing operation a crewman always stood in the wheelhouse, watching the 'meter' for the ink-strokes, between keel and seabed, that registered herring.*

The Sloans had bought the *Bairn's Pride*, which Matt was to skipper, but she'd been lying idle a while in Girvan, so it was decided to have her engine overhauled before she was taken North. Eddie McEwan's *Elizmor* was also having her engine overhauled. So the *Bairn's Pride*'s neighbour and the *Elizmor*'s neighbour – the *Wistaria* and the *Arctic Moon* respectively – paired off and went away to the Minch. When the *Bairn's Pride* and *Elizmor* were through their overhauls, they set off north too, on a Monday morning, putting into Tarbert on passage because the *Elizmor*'s engine had blown a core-plug which needed fixing.

That done, the boats carried on and just after darkness emerged from the Crinan Canal. Off Lismore, they saw two green lights, which proved to be the *Anne Marie* of Tarbert and another fishing boat, both on passage to Oban. Neither Matt Sloan nor Eddie McEwan had ever been through the inside of the notorious Torran Rocks, which lie off the Ross of Mull, so they decided they would go no further that night and went into Loch Buie and dropped anchor. They left the loch before daybreak and with the benefit of daylight steered a course inside the Torran Rocks and on through the Iona Sound into Loch Scridain.

'Ye could jeest aboot tell that there wir herrin in that loch,' Matt Sloan remembered; but he couldn't get the *Bairn's Pride*'s echo-sounder to work no matter what he tried. As they were going up along the head of the loch, one of the crew, Andy Alexander, remarked: 'Dae ye know what? That gull picked up a herrin there.' Matt Sloan at once hit the echo-meter a blow with his fist ... and it started working! Being the kind of echo-sounder it was, the recording wasn't 'white-lined', therefore, as Matt put it, 'it wis difficult tae distinguish is this herrin ye're seein or is this the bottom?' He knew, however, that they were in fairly shallow water. One of the crew unwound the feeling-wire over the side and there were herring there right enough. The net, which had been bought from William 'Bunty' McCrindle of the *Golden West*, was new and had never been used. With that net, the *Bairn's Pride* and *Elizmor* were filled and the boats were back through the Iona Sound, long before dark, and into Oban to discharge the catch.

At that time, there was no radio transmitter on the *Bairn's Pride*, but the *Elizmor* had one and Eddie McEwan heard the skippers of the *Wistaria* and *Arctic Moon* talking and learned that they were on their way to Mallaig from Loch Skiport or thereabouts with 70 cran of herring aboard each boat. Eddie couldn't contact them by radio, but a phone call was made from Oban with the message that the *Bairn's Pride* and *Elizmor* were in with the full of the boats of Loch Scridain herring and that it was advisable they come down. The four boats took fishings out of the Mull lochs for a fortnight afterwards.

Andy McCrindle

The weather – light easterly winds and frost – in the winter of 1946 was the best he ever experienced in the Minch. The crew of the *Golden West* used to cross to Mallaig at the end of every week, herring or no herring, to get stores and to lie the week-end there. The following winter's weather wasn't so good and they 'got some dustins' crossing the Minch. Andy's brother-in-law from New Zealand, Mervyn Thorburn – a Squadron Leader in the RAF during the War – thought that he would 'have a go at the fishing'. He shipped aboard the *Golden West* in 1947 and, on his first night in the North, found himself in Barra Sound in 'hard nor-west wind'. Just as the crew started to haul the net, a big hail-shower came on, the stones – half the size of golf-balls – pinging off Mervyn's ears. None the less, he stuck the job and became a partner with Andy in the *Silver Fern*, launched at Fairlie in 1950. Three years later, however, he decided that fishing wasn't for him, after all, and he went to university, took a master's degree in Science and became a schoolteacher.

Duncan Campbell

The crews of the *Moira* and *Nobles Again* were mending a net at Lochboisdale, up to their knees in snow, in December of 1953. They had been 13 weeks in the North without a break, and one of the *Nobles'* crew was seething. Finally, his temper broke. 'Is it no time we had a bloody weekend at home?' – 'Well,' said the *Moira*'s skipper, Neil Speed, in measured tones, 'if ye want a week-end at home, there's the steamer on Monday morning.'

Half-an-hour later, Neil Speed informed the unhappy man that he and his crew would be going home not only for New Year, but also for Christmas – which was unprecedented at that time – adding slyly, 'But A don't know what your skipper's going tae do.' Some time later, Neil again addressed the man: 'And I can tell you another thing – our last shot is a stoker shot. But,' he again added, 'I don't know what your skipper's going tae do.' ('Stoker' was when the proceeds of a catch were divided among the crew without deduction of the boat's shares – a lucrative perk.)

That night, the *Nobles* was sent away to market with 150 cran of herring and the *Moira* went into North Bay to lie. The crew was sitting at breakfast when a boat came alongside. 'Who's that, Kemmel?' said Neil Speed. Duncan looked and saw the neighbour-boat. 'I wis feart tae say it tae him,' he admitted. 'It's wir neebor.' – 'What!' cried Neil, vexed at this inexplicable return. He went on deck. 'Ah, Jock, what's the matter?' he said, addressing the *Nobles'* skipper. 'Oh,' Jock replied, 'a wile moarnin oot there wi snow. We canna see a finger afore us.' Neil, still angry, said that his crew would run the catch, but that hasty plan was judged unwise, and, in the end, Jock set off again, having declared that the snow showers had cleared. As Neil let go the *Nobles'* stern-rope, his parting words were: 'An don't be long tae ye're back, Jock.'

The *Nobles* duly returned for the last night of fishing. The boats were out by four o'clock in the afternoon seeking herring around the Curachan. Kemmel was on the feeling-wire all night, fortified by mugs of soup and tea, but there was nothing to be felt and he was impatient to be away home. At daylight in the morning, however, he called to Neil in the wheelhouse: 'Anything on the meter?' – 'No, nothing,' Neil replied. 'Well, stand by,' said Duncan, 'there plenty herrin here.' – 'Are ye sure?' – 'A'm sure!' – 'Well,' Neil cautioned, 'don't turn yer heid. Here's me brother jeest crossin wir stern.' This was Matthew Speed – 'Krammer' – in the *Maureen*. 'Good morning, brother,' Neil called innocently as the *Maureen* passed; and then to Duncan: 'Have ye still got them, Kemmel?' The wire was tugging Duncan's hand with the impact of the shoal.

Neil shot, but the sky to westward was suddenly seen to be 'as black as tar'. 'A've heard them sayin hailstones the size o golf ba's,' Duncan remarked. 'By Christ, they *wir* the size o golf ba's!' The force of the wind blew the *Moira* into the centre of her net, despite the neighbour-boat's effort – with engine going full power – to tow her out; but the squall passed and 176 cran of herring were brailed aboard. 'Whose on waatch gan ower?' Neil asked. 'Uncle Neil, it's you an Kemmel,' Tom Kelly replied. With that, Neil erupted: 'By God, me an Kemmel's been up aa night!' – 'It's your watch,' the crew insisted.

They took her the length of Canna. Duncan had tea and toast ready for the next watch, then he and Neil turned in. The *Moira* arrived in Oban. After the catch had been discharged and breakfast eaten, Neil sent Duncan to the fish-salesman's office to lift the money for the shot. When Duncan returned to the boat, he threw the money across the table to Neil; but Neil threw it back at him and insisted that he divide it, since he'd been the one that felt the herring. 'Hoot's it tae be – six or ten shares?' Duncan asked, as the crew kicked at him below the table. 'I said in Lochboisdale,' Neil replied, 'our last shot is a stoker shot – six shares.' Each man received £76, 'some money in them days,' as Duncan remarked. 'Right, one hour ashore,' Neil announced. 'Go an get yer Christmas presents.' Duncan bought, for each of his two daughters, a white bible, which they still have.

The crew met up with Neil in the Railway Bar, where he ordered six glasses of whisky and six half-pints of beer for 'their Christmas'. Then it was back aboard the boat for the last stage of the trip, down to Crinan. They had almost cast off, when somebody realised that a bus hadn't been ordered to take them home from Crinan. With that oversight remedied, they finally left, arriving in Crinan to discover that the bus had had a puncture and would be about an hour late … so there was nothing for it but to repair to the Crinan Hotel. There they met up with their neighbours, and when the *Nobles'* crew discovered that Neil had stokered the *Moira's* shot, they all threatened to leave Jock unless he did likewise. Jock – who skippered the boat for a Campbeltown businessman – finally had to capitulate, and Neil Speed – who hadn't been the least vocal in the matter – insisted: 'Right, Jock, that'll be eleven halfs, eleven half-pints an a glass o port tae yersel!'

Appearances

. . . .

'Appearances' were the natural signs by which ring-net fishermen judged that herring were present. These signs were many and engaged all the senses. The fishermen looked and listened and smelt the air, alert for the merest hint that might lead them to herring. At times the sign was slight indeed, perhaps a 'spittle', which was how fishermen described the sound a herring made when breaking the surface of the sea with its nose on a calm night. At other times, the sound of herring 'playing' – or rushing over the surface in a great body – could be heard miles distant. The 'herring whale', or common rorqual, which fed on herring and followed the shoals, was the greatest of the creatures which signified the prospects of a fishing, but dolphins, porpoises and seals were also useful. Basking-sharks, which shared the food of herring, were nuisances as well as indicators, and several species of bird were carefully watched. Chief of these was the gannet, and ring-net fishermen were expert in analysing its behaviour. Gulls could be observed lifting herring out of the water, and their very presence on certain parts of the coast could lead fishermen to herring when night came. The herring themselves could be seen, showing black or red, below the sea's surface in daylight, or lighting the night waters with the phosphorescent sheen that was called 'burning' or 'fire in the water'. The 'putting up' of bubbles from their swim-bladders, also revealed the herrings' deep presence to fishermen. The smell of their oil and the sheen of the oil itself on the surface were also signs.

Greatest appearance

The greatest appearance that James Macdonald ever saw was one December morning around 1950. From the Weaver's Castle south beyond the Curachan, the sky was crowded with gulls and gannets, and there were whales – 'A'd never seen so many whales in ma life' – rolling through the herring. The fishing lasted all that night and in the morning there were still boats, alerted by radio transmissions, arriving from the North Minch.

Ian Gibson, at the mouth of Barra Sound, saw a similar appearance: 'Soalid herrin on the top o the water ... an it must've been three or fower mile aheid o us. Ye wid've thought,' he added, 'that the likes o that kinna fishin wid never be extinct.'

Smelling herring

One time, going across the Minch for Mallaig, James McCreath was in the *May*'s wheelhouse alone. About three miles off Canna he called the crew – 'Come 'ere!' – and two or three of the men came on deck. He slowed the boat down. 'What's that? Dae ye feel that?' he asked. 'What?' one of them queried. 'Can ye no smell the herrin here?' – 'Naw,' the man replied. McCreath took bearings on the spot and carried on to Mallaig. There was, in the harbour, an East Coast steam-drifter whose skipper James McCreath knew, for he let McCreath bark his nets aboard the boat, which carried her own barking-tanks. There were two or three fishermen about the quay when McCreath berthed his boat, but it was Sandy, the drifter-skipper, he wanted to see before he returned across the Minch. He found him and said to him: 'A'll gie ye a tip. Mind ye, if it disna come aff, don't blame me.' He gave Sandy the distance and bearings and advised him: 'But lie here. Ye've time enough tae lie. Lie here tae once everybody's oot o sight afore ye go oot.' Sandy had about 45 cran the next day, and told the other East Coast driftermen in Mallaig who it was that tipped him off. Those among them that knew McCreath afterwards gave him a tongue-lashing! However, all the drifters fished that spot of herring right into the back of Soay for about a week and made a big fishing out of it. [James McCreath]

To judge by the following story, James McCreath had not always been convinced of the value of the nose in locating herring.

His *May* had teamed up temporarily with Willie 'Skreich' McIntyre in the *Nil Desperandum*, the respective neighbour-boats having broken down (p 21). They were dodging along north of Loch Boisdale, under sheer sea-cliffs, when somebody remarked: 'Look at that gannet – that gannet's aafu frightened!' The bird was close against the cliffs, flying with erratic movements. It was a calm day, so the two boats were brought together, and Jimmy McCreath called over: 'There naethin here. Where dae ye think we'll go?' 'Skreich' was in the wheelhouse and cried to Henry Martin, who was on the foredeck: 'Ye're very quiet up there – hoot dae you think aboot it?' – 'Well', Henry replied, 'anybody that lea's here is gan away clear o herrin.' Like a shot, McCreath queried this: 'Whit wey?' – 'A can smell them,' replied Henry. 'Well, if ye can smell herrin, that's a new yin on me,' McCreath said. 'A've heard many's a thing, but A never heard anybody sayin they could smell them.' They waited and early in the evening herring started jumping. They shot and got a good ring as close to the rocks as they could safely go. McCreath was ecstatic: 'There a man can smell them!'

The fishing was slack that night and the catch fetched a high price in Mallaig. They returned to the same place the following day and there was a fleet of boats there. But the sea was 'polluted' with smeltings (fish-oil-slicks) and an oily smell hung in the air. McCreath came alongside and quickly engaged Henry Martin: 'Martin, there's no doubt that the smellin business is a' right there. Are ye smellin that?' – 'That's gleshans – that's no herrin.' This was a case of chancing a judgement, though he did think the smell very strong to be emanating from herring. The *Nobles* and the *Silver Grey* of Campbeltown shot and, sure enough – about 100 baskets of small saithe in the net. That 'killed' McCreath! [Henry Martin]

A cormorant with a herring in its mouth

On one occasion the Sloans were coming south from Loch Maddy with the *Bairn's Pride* and the *Wistaria*, and before they reached the North Fords, they went into a place which they knew existed, though they had never been in it before. They took the north channel in – its breadth was only about twice the beam of the boat, and a bottom of rocks and tangles could be clearly seen – and found themselves in a wide basin. Once in, they went round and round that basin. There were gulls about it and two or three scarts diving, and the men were all convinced that they could smell fish. Round and round they went. They unwound the feeling-wire, they checked the echo-meter, but neither felt nor saw any sign of herring. Then, ahead of the boat, a scart (cormorant) surfaced with a herring in its mouth. They shot the net around the bird and netted 160 cran of herring. The crew were amazed. They couldn't think it possible to go round a basin – so confined an area that only three or four nets could have been shot in it – and criss-cross it over and over again with a wire and a sounder going and not locate a thing. The assumption was that something – perhaps the engines – had disturbed the shoal. [Matt Sloan]

A seal with a herring in its mouth

The *Kathleen* of Campbeltown was heading through the Sound of Kerrera – by no means regarded as a herring-fishing ground – on passage to Loch Buie, Mull, in the winter of 1953. As Duncan Campbell took a cup of tea up to the skipper, Willie 'Toon' MacDonald, in the wheelhouse, he happened to turn and saw a seal surface with a herring in its mouth. 'Toon's' response, when Duncan told him, was instantaneous: 'Oh, that's good enough!' He shot and filled both the *Kathleen* and one of her neighbours, the *Mary McLean* (the other in the threesome was the *Golden Hind*, skippered by Willie's brother, Duncan). The catch was discharged, at Oban, into a Dutch Klondyker. While Duncan was aboard the vessel, one of her crew asked him if he wanted to buy whisky. Duncan asked the price and was told, 'Ten shillings'. He took two bottles and was then offered a pair of seaboots at the same price, so he bought these too. [Duncan Campbell]

Herring playing

The Jacksons were 'four boats' – ie, two pairs of boats in partnership – with Willie 'Gorrie' McCaffer. They were steaming by the mouth of North Bay and there was nothing doing, so the four boats – the *Village Maid*, the *Village Belle*, the *Evelyn* and the *Anne Marie* – tied alongside one another, stopped the engines and the crews had a yarn while the boats drifted. Suddenly herring were heard 'garrin' – playing loudly – ahead of the boats. When the echo-meters were checked, the shoal was seen to be 'top and bottom', that is, registering from keel to seabed. One of the boats rounded up and shot – 300 cran in the net. Half of the shot was taken aboard the *Village Belle* and the other half aboard the *Evelyn* – there was a quota of 150 cran at the time – and they set off for market, leaving the other pair to continue fishing. [Neil Jackson]

'Roarin oot the water ...'

One 'fine, clear, calm night', the *Silver Fern* was steaming south of Muldonich. There wasn't much doing and Alex Rae was standing outside the wheelhouse. The skipper, Andy McCrindle, had the window open and suddenly Alex said to him: 'Ye hear that noise?' Andy slowed the boat down and the two men could hear the herring 'roarin oot the water aw roon aboot us'. The echo-meter, when checked, revealed a shoal extending 'fae top tae bottom'. Andy turned and shot the net 'roon the whole bloomin lot'. His crew and the neighbouring crew, from Eddie McEwan's *Elizmor*, couldn't cope, and a Girvan pair, Sandy Forbes's *Betty* and Campbell McCreath's *Erica*, were summoned; but the combined effort of the four crews was likewise futile and the catch went to the bottom and was lost. [Andy McCrindle]

A play of scallops

The *Enterprise* of Campbeltown almost shot on a play of swimming creachans (queen scallops, *Chlamys opercularis*) one evening off the Stac at Canna. The shellfish were 'as black as tar gan off on top o the watter' and sounded not unlike herring rushing; but Alex Black shrewdly advised: 'That's them bloody creachans.' He'd been present, years before, when the *Lochfyne* shot at daybreak one Saturday in the Lodan, south of Campbeltown. Old Malcolm McLean remarked, when the crew of the *Enterprise* jumped aboard to help haul the net: 'Wile funny herrin playin.' The two crews took until two o'clock in the afternoon getting the shellfish up and the net cleared of them! [Duncan Campbell]

Putting-up – the redeemer that never was

The *Lily* of Campbeltown, neighbouring the *Fionnaghal* of Tarbert, had been nearly a month in the North with next to nothing to show for it. They had hunted fruitlessly from Loch Dunvegan to Loch Pooltiel and down to Loch Bracadale. The crews agreed they'd be just as well to go home, but would give the Canna grounds a look on the way. The boats went out to the Heisgeir to see what was doing there. Young Davie McNaughton was sitting forward with John 'Glindy' McKinlay, watching the sail-fish around the boat, when they came into a patch of putting-up – the sea was just 'frying' with the density of the bubbles! 'Glindy', seeing this, began shouting at the top of his voice: 'It's the big yins! It's a redeemer! It's a redeemer!'

The net was shot right away, the boats met and hauling began. At first the signs were promising – the flotation buoys along the top of the bag were dipping with the weight of something netted – but the crews' elation was short-lived, because not a herring was to be seen all the time the net was being taken aboard. But there was a catch of some kind, and, as the bag was being dried up, it became apparent what it was – horse mackerel, about 120 cran of horse mackerel, for which there was no market. Poor 'Glindy' was almost in tears and kicking at the gunwale in sheer frustration. [David McNaughton]

A mistake corrected

The brothers Matt and Billy Sloan were lying forward together on a summer's day south-west of the Heisgeir. Billy, who had just joined the crew, said to his brother: 'What's that? There bubbles comin up there.' – 'Och,' Matt replied casually, 'that's nothing tae worry aboot. There a lot o dookers aboot an that's them – they've dived an it's the bubbles comin up fae them.' But Matt took another look and saw that the appearance was going on and on. 'Oh,' he said, realising his error, 'it's herrin puttin up.' They were rewarded with 75 cran. The boat was the *Virginia*, which was attached to a Girvan pair, the McCreath brothers' *May* and *Southern Sun*, while the *Veronica*, which eventually became the *Virginia*'s neighbour, was being built. [Matt Sloan]

A netful in the Anchorage

The biggest ring that Hugh Edgar ever saw was in the South Anchorage of Loch Boisdale and it was also the only time he ever saw a ring-net shot there. He was steaming out from Lochboisdale pier with the *Hercules* one afternoon in January of 1965 or '66, when one of the crew – his cousin, Robert 'Dobbin' Gibson – remarked: 'Whit's that ower there?' It was bird activity over herring that were 'pittin up'. There's a lot of hard ground about the Anchorage, so Hugh shot the net in a tight circle and picked up his own end, otherwise, as he remarked, the net would have 'got a doin' on the ground. There were a couple of intoxicated 'Heilanders' out in a big coble gathering wrack for the seaweed-processing plant at Girvan – loads of the stuff were periodically shipped away by puffer – and they came aboard the *Hercules* to give a hand with the hauling. 'When we wid get the soles up, the herrin wir green. It's the biggest ever A seen. A don'know whoot wid be in thon – a thoosan cran?' But the net burst after a couple of hundred cran had been brailed out of it, though the only damage was to the after sole-deepening, or bottom net-guard. The *Hercules* was working, at that time, in a foursome with the *Marie*, *Golden Venture* and *Taeping*. [Hugh Edgar]

Too many

One Friday night, in the mid-50s, the Sloans were returning, with the *Watchful* and the *Wistaria*, across the Minch from the market at Oban heading for Muldonich. Listening to the chat on the radio, Matt gathered that several boats had been ringing backwards and forwards from the Curachan down to Muldonich, offshore a bit and in deep water.

Spots of herring could be heard playing on the surface and were showing too on the echo-meter, but they were nearly impossible to catch – somebody would mark a herring or two, somebody else would get a basket and another fellow maybe a cran.

About 15 or 20 minutes before the Sloans got in on these boats, Matt and his crew saw something in the water to the north. The night was calm and moonlit and what they saw was like a puff of wind on the water, creating a kind of darkness. 'Whit's that?' one of the crew said. 'That's lik a puff o wind.' Yet there was no wind. Matt slowed the boat and canted to starboard towards the appearance. It was a shoal of herring playing, 'literally solid', and sounding like a gale of wind. They shot round about the spot, remarking, as they did, that if they'd had a brailer hanging over the side of the boat, they could have filled it with the fish swimming alongside.

Matt's brother and fishing partner, Billy, spoke to Grieve Gemmell, skipper of the *Storm Drift*, and Grieve told him: 'This is what's been goin on aw night, Billy. The boats've been ringin here, herrin playin an seein spots on the meter, an there's nobody's got anythin worthwhile. Of course,' he added, 'it'll go on tae somebody gets them, an when they get them they'll likely get too many.' And that's exactly what happened. By the time the other boats came off, the soles were up and the net closed. The Sloans had almost finished filling their boats when the sling burst and the herring left in the net were lost before any of the other crews could come alongside and get a share. Later on, Grieve remarked to Billy: 'There ye are. Ye know what A said tae ye? It'll go on lik this tae some'dy gets them, an they'll likely get too many.' [Matt Sloan]

Burning

The Sloans were seldom in the Minch after mid-June, but in one particular year they were working on the Curachan Bank at the end of July, and that was a 'burnin fishin'. With the short nights, they 'had aboot time tae get a couple o rings wi the burnin an that wis yer burnin time in'. The fishermen did notice 'that wee bit extra light' as they went north, and it was possible in the Minch to read a newspaper on deck at midnight. Matt Sloan recalled having two or three rings with burning near the lit headland of Uisenis, north of Scalpay-Harris, during one winter. Winter burning, however, is a rare phenomenon. On these occasions, he speculated, the phosphorescence might have been generated by the bulk and density of the herring shoals. 'There wis a big spot there and they showed up better, somehow or another.' [Matt Sloan]

Tommy Ralston, in My Captains, *p 27, records a similar instance of winter burning in the Minch.*

In Loch Pooltiel

Some fishermen were skilled at detecting herring in the phosphorescence and others weren't. Deep herring were particularly difficult to discern. 'You would have thought it changed the water – just kinna white – an if you werena up to it, you winnae have seen it at all,' as James McCreath explained. He recalled coming out of Loch Pooltiel, Skye, one night and going in along the cliffs as close as the boat could safely go. It was James McCreath's practice, when looking for herring in the burning, to put one of the crew in the wheelhouse and to go on to the boat's bow himself to watch the water. This night, he 'touched the anchor' – knocking it to start the herring moving – and said to the fellow beside him: 'Dae ye see anything there?' – 'Naw,' was the decisive reply. James let the boat go about half the length of a net, then shouted to the man in the wheel-house: 'Bring her roon an put the winky away!' They got a fine fishing, but the man who was with him on the bow afterwards remarked: 'I never saw nothin!' – 'Well,' James replied, 'I seen them.' [James McCreath]

A swirl of tide with red feeding

'Red feeding' described dense concentrations of the minute copepods, in partic-ular Calanus, *on which herring fed. The redness is caused by oil in a sac along the gut. That oil is ordinarily colourless, or faint pink at most, but occasionally the colour is greatly intensified so that dense lumps of these minute cructaceans appear red. These lumps of copepods moved with the wind and would be followed by herring and followed too by fishermen, who knew that where the feeding was, herring too were likely to be.*

'The only other incident of note I remember from 1938 was one evening down off Vatersay. We had shot on a good spot of herring, but had hardly started to boat the net when a swirl of tide came from nowhere and knocked the net completely out of shape; but there was a spot of red feeding in the middle of the swirl and we could see some herring glancing below it. Eventually we got the net into shape and, much to our surprise, dried up about 80 cran. The feeding kept the herring in the net, despite the shape it was in.' [Neil Short, letter]

A black lump

Herring shoals could be located in winter when they showed as 'black lumps' swimming over a sandy seabed, but Andy McCrindle of Maidens once rung on a curious concentration of stationary herring. He was in the Fords with the *Silver Fern*, neighbouring the *May Queen*, one afternoon, and the boats were looking for herring in two or three fathoms of water. The herring they found were packed level in a 'wee depression' in the seabed, and the spot yielded about 90 cran. [Andy McCrindle]

Gannets

● ● ● ● ● ● ● ● ● ● ●

Gannets – giss, for 'solan geese', to the Ayrshire fishermen – were one of the main signs of herring, both in the Minch and in home waters, and fishermen always studied their behaviour. The gannet is distinguishable from all other seabirds by its stiff-winged flight and pure white plumage, which can be seen from miles away particularly when sunshine catches it. The gannet remained valuable to ring-net fishermen right to the demise of the method.

Observations on behaviour

It was said that the best time to get a gannet was in the gloaming, 'because the gannet wis actually seein somethin worthwhile when he struck'. Andy Alexander saw ring-nets shot through the day on gannets striking and 'ye wouldnae mark a fish'. If a gannet struck, fishermen would always wait to see if he came back and struck on that spot again, and if he did they always took that spot because they were certain 'there wis somethin there'. A gannet striking and then flying away might signify a single fish. The best sign was when gannets would 'hang an bend thir nebs doon an then a straight dive'. A gannet 'skliffin' – diving at an angle – was judged to be on 'a mackerel dive', and if gannets were striking 'too often', then that too was attributed to their feeding on mackerel. One of the advantages of ringing on gannets was that the herring weren't disturbed. 'Say you saw a gannet strikin an ye went through where it had struck,' Andy Alexander observed, 'ye wid probably see a mark o fish [on the echometer], but at the same time ye must've disturbed it.' And by the time the net has been shot around the spot of herring, the fish have been disturbed yet again. Often, therefore, it paid to shoot round a gannet without confirming, with the echo-sounder, that herring were present, especially in the summer fishing in the North when the herring appeared to be in small feeding 'balls', or shoals. [Andy Alexander]

If the gannet was striking deep, straight down, the fishermen knew that he was working on deep herring; but if he was striking at a slant from no great height, then they would say, 'That's macherel he's strikin on', because mackerel were always more to the surface. Fishermen believed that the gannet would single out a fish before committing himself to a strike. Sometimes a bird would be seen circling and circling and circling, and Sammy Gemmell would watch this and pronounce on it: 'Well, that could be a big spoat o fish.' His interpretation was that the bird was singling out a fish, perhaps watching for the edge of the shoal, because gannets didn't strike 'willy-nilly'. Then, if he did strike, the fishermen would ring there. 'Sometims ye wid get a big ring an sometims ye winna get very mony, A daresay.' Along big cliffs, such as in Moonen Bay, gannets might be seen gliding on the updraught from the sea, but these birds signified nothing to the fishermen. They were just enjoying themselves, gliding round about. The fishermen had a term for it. Sammy, leaning out of the wheelhouse window, would remark: 'Ach, that bird's jeest eddyin there.' The gannet wasn't looking for fish at all. If he had been, his head would have been down. Moonen Bay, Scour Bay, and Canna were all gannet fishing grounds in the summer. [Grieve Gemmell]

The summer fishing in the Minch lasted from late April, through May and June, and then the fleet shifted to the Isle of Man. In the North, going into a bight or searching the shore, if a gannet struck then a crew would ring on that gannet. At times a crew might be fooled – the gannet could be on sand-eels or a 'rogue' herring, a wanderer – but if that gannet struck, rose, wheeled about and returned to strike on the same spot, then assuredly there was no rogue involved. In that spring-summer fishing, the fishermen felt that if they could shoot the net around a spot of herring without actually going through it and disturbing the fish, then they had gained an advantage. Gannets were considered very reliable indicators of herring. Even later in the year, if a gannet was seen along the shore in late afternoon, a crew would watch that place, because herring sought the shore when darkness was coming down. [Matt Sloan]

Sixteen rings for nothing

Fishing on gannets was a rather chancy operation. If you got it right, you made a good job of it, but more frequently you could get it wrong, either by failing to get the net around the gannet or misjudging the set of the tide. The best time to shoot on a gannet was just at the close of the evening when the birds were usually higher and more inclined to succeed in their dive. On one occasion, the *New Dawn* and *Fair Morn* were fishing on gannets in Scour Bay, Skye. The crews, starting at one o'clock in the afternoon, had no fewer than 16 rings, one after the other in rapid succession, and all for nothing. The men were becoming exhausted and demoralised, when, just as the sun was going down, the *Fair Morn* shot and this time the effort was rewarded with 80 cran, much to the relief of everyone. [Iain Gemmell]

Regurgitating herring

The summer fishing was the gannet fishing. If the fishermen saw a gannet sitting in the water, somebody would say, 'That gannet's full up'. And if he couldn't rise, they would chase him with the boat. He would start vomiting herring and perhaps two or three fish would come up before he had lightened himself enough to take off. 'Aye, what kinna herrin?' – 'Aw, they're guid herrin this bird's pittin up.' Thus satisfied, the crews would remain in that area until darkness came and they could begin looking for herring. [Grieve Gemmell]

Spring gannets

The *Silver Fern* and *Silver Lining* of Maidens were crossing from Canna one spring day in the late 1950s and struck in on the West Side north of the Stuleys. The boats were still 'a good bit off' when one of the *Silver Fern*'s crew remarked to his skipper, Andy McCrindle: 'A gannet struck there, jeest aboot half-a-mile ahead o us, in there, in on the shore.' Andy headed in, and, just where the bird had dived, saw, on the echo-meter, 'a wee stroke'. He shot round the spot and the net came fast, but then 'jumped' clear of the snag and the crews hauled 150 cran of herring. They were just taking the catch aboard when the *Wistaria* and *Watchful* appeared, but there had just been the one spot of herring and the Sloans had no success. The McCrindle pair crossed to Mallaig and discharged the catch. On their way back across, they were passing the Stac at Canna when another gannet struck – 150 cran again, though that lot had mackerel mixed through it, which necessitated a good deal of picking to remove. Then it was back to the market at Mallaig once more. 'A think,' said Andy, 'it wis the only spring fishin we ever made any money at.' [Andy McCrindle]

Silly gannets

The *Nobles* was put out of Dunvegan harbour one day, to allow a puffer to come in and discharge its cargo. The boats' boys were ashore at the time getting stores and Alec McBride in the neighbouring *Glen Carradale* said that he would wait for them returning. The *Nobles* headed south and came across the Jacksons bailing a good fishing off Dunvegan Head. This was at 12 o'clock in the day. The crew was idly watching a gannet rising out the water and dropping in again. With high gannets, you knew the herring were deep, but the gannets that day were going along the surface, and the assumption was that they were lifting dead herring that had drifted clear of the Jacksons' net. It didn't look promising, so the crew decided to have something to eat, and, in the absence of the cook, Archie Campbell, who was following in the neighbour-boat, Davie McNaughton went below to heat soup. The next thing, to the consternation of the *Nobles*' crew, Alec McBride shot away on this 'silly gannet'. But the bird wasn't so silly after all – there were 40 cran of herring in the net. Every pair after that was chasing gannets all day long. There was a herring-carrier – a drifter – in Pooltiel that the boats sold into, and that was where the catch was taken. The men finally sat down to their broth at one o'clock in the morning in Pooltiel, 12 hours after Davie first put the pot on to heat. [David McNaughton]

Shooting over the weather in the Summer Isles

When the *Nobles* and the *Glen Carradale* arrived on the fishing grounds at the Summer Isles, there was a big fleet there, but no fishing going on. They went into the middle of the fleet and began hunting for herring. Davie McNaughton was 'wire-man' on the *Nobles*, but was feeling nothing. There was only one gannet to be seen, and all the boats were 'makin a fleck' for it – hastening towards it. The skipper of the *Nobles*, Duncan McSporran, opened a window in the wheelhouse and gave Davie the order: 'If that bloody gannet goes, shot the bow.' Away indeed went the gannet, into a dive, and Duncan shouted: 'Right – away!'.

Davie McNaughton discarded the feeling-wire over the side, threw out the end-buoy, and the net began to stream over the quarter. But – exceptionally – it was streaming over the starboard quarter, not the port quarter, and the crew, standing forward on the boat, were taken by surprise; but one of them ran aft to manage the shooting of the sole-rope. The net was being shot 'back to front' or 'over the weather', for the reason that, had the skipper decided to shoot in the conventional manner

– which was over the port side – he would have had to manoeuvre into a suitable position and would thereby, in the press of other boats homing in on the gannet, have lost not only time but also his advantage. But there was an oversight in the rush to get the net out – on the starboard side of the boat there was a thole-pin shipped in the gunwale for leading the neighbour-boat's tow-rope when boating the net. The netting, as it ran out, was catching on that pin, and Davie could hear it ripping. He managed to knock out the thole-pin, but, as he did so, Duncan McSporran happened to see him in the act, and that was a row, because the thole-pin was lost. When the net was hauled, there were 60 cran in it.

One of the top Ayrshire skippers came alongside and began shouting abuse at the crews, who had nipped in ahead of him by shooting the net 'back to front'. 'Ye're naw supposed tae dae that!' he roared; but big Neil Speed forcefully pointed out that the East Coast boats habitually shot their nets over the starboard side and demanded to know what difference it made. In the end, the Ayrshireman conceded defeat and the last word was Neil's: 'It's youse that wis wrang. Youse got caught. Youse wir aa lined up there tae dodge for the gannet. We took it the opposite wey roon.' [David McNaughton]

Gulls
· · · · · · · ·

The humble seagull, of whatever species, often guided fishermen to herring, whether by its excited presence over a shoal swimming close to the surface, its practice of swooping to pluck a fish from the water, or its habit of congregating expectantly with other gulls on certain parts of the coast.

A black-backed gull

The year was 1953 and Hector Gilchrist's *Maureen* and her neighbour, the *Annie*, had left Stornoway and were heading south past the sea lochs on the east side of Lewis. The men were familiar with most of these lochs, but had never been in Loch Ouirn, so they decided they would give it a look. It was a glass-calm winter's day in the loch, but there was no appearance of herring there. A big black-backed gull was sitting out in the middle of the loch, and for 'hellment' more than anything else, Duncan Blair remarked to the *Maureen*'s skipper, Matthew Speed: 'Dae ye see that

black gull oot there, Matha?' – 'Aye.' – 'Bate ye he's sittin on a moun-
tain o herrin.' – 'Dae ye think so?' Mattha says. 'A'm near bloody sure
o it.' – 'By Christ,' Mattha replied, 'we'll go out an have a look.'

So out they went, to where the gull was sitting, and sure enough, they
saw a mass of herring on the echo-meter. The shoal was the size of a
matchbox on the recording paper, but it was deep, too deep to shoot on,
because if you shoot a net on herring 10 fathoms down, it's only the skim-
mings you would get, unless you sunk the net. In any case, they carried
on up through the loch with the echo-sounder going all the time, but
these were the only herring seen. They were looking at other boats
passing down the loch, all except an East Coast drifter coming up. Her
skipper hailed them: 'Well, boys, did ye see onythin lik herrin?' – 'Naw.
No appearance. Very very quiet-lookin,' the Campbeltown men told
him, lying, of course. This was early in the day, about 12 o'clock, and
they thought that perhaps the drifter would turn and go back out the
loch, but he saw the ring-net boats lying and, whether dubious about
what he had been told, he too lay.

The dinner was ready by this time and the crew went below to eat,
leaving Duncan Blair in the wheelhouse to 'jog about' with the echo-
sounder going all the time. The water was getting shallower as the boat
moved up the loch. Suddenly a spot of herring appeared on the meter.
The crew was still below, so Duncan gave them a shout: 'Ye'd better
come up till we try this!' They tried a shot and got about 70 cran of
herring. The drifter, seeing this, came along. 'Aye,' the skipper called,
'ye've got quite a nice shot there. How did ye get on?' – 'Oh,' said
Duncan, 'we got aboot seeventy cran.' – 'What sort o herrin are they –
good herrin?' – 'Oh, nice herrin.' – 'Aye,' the drifter skipper replied,
'that's very good – a good start.'

It came late evening, 'right shottin time', and the ringers happened to
cross to the starboard side of the loch. With the ring-net, you had to be
in a certain position before you could say, 'Right – shot!' A ring-net – at
least, among West Coast fishermen – was almost invariably shot over the
port side. The boats were therefore going the right way. They were going
up the loch when they came into a fine spot of herring, and they had
nothing to do, when they ran out of the herring, but shoot the net about
a 100 fathoms outside of where they were seeing them, and shoot her
straight. The neighbour-boat picked up the winky and started towing in
for the shore, keeping the net wide open. Then both boats got the searchlights to play on the shore and kept splashing the top of the water, to
chase the herring out off the shore. The crews took about 120 cran out
of the net and finished up with 180 or 190 cran.

On the way out the loch, they spoke again to the drifter. Snow had begun to fall and a nasty night was in prospect. 'Well, boys,' the drifter skipper said, 'ye got another good ring there.' – 'Yes,' Duncan replied, 'we got a good ring. We've got aboot close on two hunner cran in her now.' – 'An where are ye makin for?' – 'Gairloch.' – 'Ye'll have a nasty night goin across there.' – 'Oh, aye,' Duncan agreed, 'but we'll manage all right. You'll be needin help to lift that train o yours themorra,' Duncan called to the drifter skipper, kidding him on. By this time the drifter had shot all his nets. Away the *Maureen* went for Gairloch and got a good price there for the herring. Later, the drift-net crew took four baskets – a cran – of herring out of their nets!

'Now, we must've got the two spots of herrin that wis in the loch,' said Duncan Blair, analysing the sequence of events 20 years after that night. 'They must've divided themselves intae two spots, an we got the furst o them in the furst ring an got the last o them in the last ring, because the whole Campbeltown fleet that wis up there at the time herried that loch for two or three days efter that an there waarna another herring caught. So, it jeest shows ye – if ye're lucky, ye're right, an if ye're naw lucky ye can be jeest that nick off it all the time.' [Duncan Blair]

Dropped from the air

The Jackson brothers were steaming into Bay Harty one night. The moon was full and so bright that it was like daylight there; but it's usually hard to catch herring on the shore with a full moon. Neil Jackson, in the wheelhouse of the *Village Belle*, thought to himself, 'I wonder will there be any in here?' Just with that he heard a flapping on the deck and looked down, and there was a living herring. Probably a gull had lifted it out the water and then dropped it. They got a fishing no bother – the herring were playing in solid lumps and 'garrin [roaring] tae the moon'. [Neil Jackson]

The Weaver's Castle

One of the boats belonging to the MacKinnons of Eriskay was on the slipway at Mallaig for repairs, and the crew had gone across with her. The repairs, however, were going to take a bit longer than anticipated, and one day, when the *Virginia* was in Mallaig, these men approached the Ayrshire crew and asked if they were going back across to the West Side. They said that they were, and the Eriskaymen asked if they would be good enough to give them a passage across, if possible to Eriskay, but if not to Eriskay then to Lochboisdale, because they could get back down to Eriskay conveniently from there. The Sloans took them all the way home. They had never been into Eriskay harbour until that day, but the Eriskaymen showed them the way, which suited the Ayrshiremen fine – it was a little more knowledge that they had gained.

During the passage, one of these native fishermen told them that if there were no gulls to be seen at the Weaver's Castle – a ruin that sits on a big rock outcrop on the south end of Eriskay – then there would be no herring got in Barra Sound. Matt Sloan reckoned there was truth in the observation and he used to watch for gulls, not only there, but further south in the Curachan. If gulls were seen in the Curachan during the afternoon, the expectation would be: 'There herrin aboot here. We'll probably get them in North Bay tonight or in at Brevig'. 'Yes, A'm sure the majority o us paid attention tae aw these things,' he remarked. [Matt Sloan]

'Ye're a Communist!'

The first time Grieve Gemmell can recall shooting a net in Bay Askaig – just south of Bay Harty – he went in through the bight and saw nothing but three gulls sitting on a rock. It was evening and not yet dark. He decided, on an impulse, to turn back, and his father, who was with him in the wheelhouse, queried the move: 'Where are ye gaun?' Grieve replied: 'A'm goin back tae have a look in that bicht.' – 'Whit fir?' – 'There's three gulls sittin in that corner there.' His father looked at him in disgust, decried him for a 'flippin nitwit' – or perhaps something more extreme – and left the wheelhouse, the door slamming shut behind him. Grieve argued with him, but the exchange was cut short when his father pronounced the judgement: 'Right – ye're a Communist!' That particular epithet, in Sammy Gemmell's book, signalled the end of any discussion. Anyway, back in through the bight they went, located herring, shot, and got a fine fishing! [Grieve Gemmell]

Whales
· · · · · · · · · ·

*The main species of whale which led fishermen to herring appears to have been the common rorqual (*Balaenoptera physalus*), also known as the 'herring whale'. Though a baleen whale, it does not feed entirely by straining small cructacea, but will eat fish. The problem of identification arises from the fishermen's having no specific names to separate the various types of whale they encountered.*

A Whale in the Ring

'I remember one early evening in North Tarbert Bay in Canna we had shot on a spot of herring rushing. We had just started to boat the net when a whale blew on one side of the net, blew in the middle of the net, then blew on the other side of the net. We searched the net looking for holes, but couldn't find any, so the whale must have gone in between the soles and come back out the same way. We got only a few cran that time, so I suppose the whale chased most of the herring out of the net.' [Neil Short, letter]

Grieve Gemmell saw a netted whale only once, 'and we definitely rung that whale in'. It was just swimming round and round inside the ring, not looking as though it would do any damage, so Sammy Gemmell ordered the sole to be slackened out, thus reversing the closure of the net. Immediately the whale came to the gap in the soles, it 'soomed awa through below the boat'. [Grieve Gemmell]

A whale throwing herring off its back

'I was back in the North in the winter of 1945. News came in of some good shots being got in the Loch Eynort area and we set off this time with the *King Bird*, *King Fisher*, *Kittiwake* and *Felicia*. This was the *Kittiwake*'s first time back at the fishing after war service, and the *Felicia*'s neighbour was at the seine-net. That was the winter I saw for the first and only time a whale throwing herring off its back. We were coming down from Loch Skiport to Loch Boisdale to land some herring aboard the *Craighaugh*, when just outside the loch we saw this whale. Each time it blew, it threw the herring feet into the air, and a mass of herring flowed down its sides like water tumbling over a waterfall. It was some sight, and just as I had heard it described by my Father and other men of that generation.

'We came out in the late afternoon and finished up with something over 300 crans. We could have filled the boats but were a bit wary of the weather. I should explain that the *Craighaugh* was an East Coast steam-drifter, chartered by George Duncan, a Mallaig buyer, to buy herring on the ground, so to speak, and run them to Mallaig. We got a number of good shots after that, mostly down in Barra Sound, the biggest being a bit over 400 cran from one ring. That was about the end of the fishing that winter and we were home, I think, towards the end of November. A successful trip altogether.' [Neil Short, letter]

Attempting to enter a net

Neil Jackson, at Canna, once saw a whale attempt, he supposed, to enter the net. It was reckoned that the whale was smelling the herring through the net, and he was round and round the boats before coming up to the net 'for a look'; but the crews made a racket and chased him away. [Neil Jackson]

A cruel trick

Duncan MacInnes was told an appalling story concerning the treatment of a herring whale, or 'cullach', in Loch Dunvegan, Skye. There was a fleet of boats drift-netting in the loch and a whale appeared among them. Some of the fishermen began feeding herring to the whale, 'and it seemed quite happy till some idiot decided he would have his bit of fun. The moment the whale surfaced and opened his huge mouth, the fool threw a shovelful of red-hot cinders into the whale's mouth'. At that, all hell broke loose, with a frightening noise coming from the whale as it rampaged around the boats, rolling in the nets and churning the water. Four or five boats lost all or most of their nets, including the Buckie boat to which the culprit belonged. He, however, was not himself from Buckie, but a native, and the boat's skipper had to put him ashore for his own safety, because the other fishermen 'would have killed him'. [Duncan MacInnes, letter]

Sharks

· · · · · · · · ·

The general name for the basking-shark among Clyde fishermen was sail-fish, but the prevalent name among Tarbert crews was sholter, from Gaelic seòldair, or 'sailor'. Muldoan was not commonly used and was considered to be, as one Ayrshire fisherman put it, 'a Teuchter name'. The basking shark, which can approach 30ft (9.14m) in length and weigh six tons, is the second-largest fish in the world and has been hunted for centuries, principally for the oil its huge liver contains. It is, however, a plankton-feeder and harmless to humans unless inadvertently capsizing a small boat.

A nuisance

The way the summer fishing was done in the North, you'd to go to a lee shore to get herring because the wind would blow the feeding in, and basking-sharks would be in with the feeding too. In Canna, the sharks were so thick that, as Archibald Stewart remarked, 'ye'd tae try an make a wee passage for tae get through them an shot'. You would get them in the nets too and have 'a hell of a job tae get them clear'. Robert McGown had a ring-net almost ruined by a basking shark in Loch Vatten; then the slime off the shark would rot the net away and the netting where the fish had gone through would have to be cut out and replaced. Neil Jackson saw his father shoot in Shepherd's Bay and counted 50 'shollters' in and around the net. As the crews closed the net, they were chasing the sharks out with poles. Angus McCrindle reckoned that once the glit (slime) or the smell of a shark was on a net, you'd always get another shark with that net. Fishermen tried pouring diesel oil over the net, to 'kill the glit', but it never worked.

A superstition

Jock Meenan of Campbeltown and Billy Sloan of Maidens had a great rapport. They were always yarning at the week-end when they'd find themselves in the same place. Jock was firmly of the opinion that it was dangerous even to talk about sail-fish, because even talking about them meant you'd get one in the net. One week-end in Lochboisdale, Jock and Billy were conversing with great earnestness, but overheard by Billy's brother Matt and another Ayrshireman, Tam Harvey. 'A huvnae heard anybody mention sail-fish yet,' Matt interjected. Jock Meenan wasn't at all pleased. Anyway, the Sloans went out on the Monday afternoon, shot on a gannet out at the back of Muldonich and netted a sail-fish! Said Billy to Matt, not, perhaps, without some bitter satisfaction: 'That's what ye get – Jock Meenan tellt ye!' [Matt Sloan]

A fast-moving sail-fish

'The summer of 1938 we were back in Canna, fishing there and over in Rum, and then moving on maybe over to Skye or out to the Boisdale side. As far as I remember it was just the usual – some weeks quite good and some slack. I remember one day in Canna, we were making for South Tarbert Bay and came on a pair boating a net. Right in the middle of the net was a sail-fish, and, as we watched, it gave two or three lashes of its tail and charged right at the centre of the net, broke the back-rope – flinging it into the air – and left a very dirty tear in the net. I never thought sail-fish could move so fast.' [Neil Short, letter]

A Norwegian

Matt Sloan watched a Norwegian shark-catcher at work 'high off Corodale' one day, and the entire operation, from the harpooning of the shark until its carcase – minus liver – was dropped away, took just 10 minutes. [Matt Sloan]

An experiment in harpooning

Iain Gemmell's initial spring fishing in the North, in 1950, was the first time – probably the last time – that he saw sail-fish in vast numbers. The boats were in Moonen Bay, Skye, and the crews couldn't shoot the nets as a consequence of the density of the sharks. There was abundant herring to be seen, but no way of getting a net around them without doing damage. The Gemmells had tried twice and torn both nets with sail-fish going through them. The boats were lying tied together in the bay, their crews wondering what to do. This particular day, the older men were below and the boys alone on deck, so the boys decided to experiment in harpooning a sail-fish. There was a bayonet aboard, which was used – attached to a pole – for clearing the propellor, when fouled. They lashed that bayonet to the *Summer Rose*'s boathook and did, indeed, harpoon a sail-fish, but unfortunately for them they had forgotten to fasten the harpoon-line to the boat. The last they saw of the bayonet and boathook, they were sticking out of the sail-fish as it charged through the bay, trying to free itself of the device. The boys had to hurriedly fashion a replacement, which was, to the older men's annoyance, much inferior to the one that was rashly lost. [Iain Gemmell]

Rubbing their backs

On two or three occasions at the Heisgeir, when the boat was lying stopped, the crew waiting for evening coming and the commencement of fishing, the boat could be felt swaying, as though touching ground; this on a dead calm sea. 'Ye'd sorta gie a wee stagger' with the unexpected motion, Davie McNaughton recalled. His father, Dan, and the skipper, Duncan McSporran, explained that this was a basking-shark rubbing its back along the boat's keel to free itself of 'lice'. 'That's the big fellas scratchin thir back,' the older men would say. 'Many's the time,' Davie said, 'A used tae see them comin oot the watter, on thir backs.' The fishermen believed that too was the sharks ridding themselves of lice. [David McNaughton]

Diesel as a deterrent

At times, Robert Ross recalled, 'ye couldn't sail through them'. Some crews carried a forty-gallon barrel of diesel oil, and when they'd be shooting the net they were decanting the diesel over the side to leave a trail of fuel in the water. The theory was that the shollter coming along feeding, with his mouth wide open, would taste or smell the diesel and turn away clear of the net. [Robert Ross]

Fishing

Fishing and fishermen

As one who spent 16 years on the deck of Billy Sloan's *Wistaria*, Hugh McPhee is singularly well-qualified to discuss the qualities that make a good fisherman, for the Sloan brothers were among the most successful of post-war ring-net skippers. Highly dedicated and highly skilled, 'the one complemented the other'. He reckoned that he made more money in his 16 years with the Sloans than in his subsequent 30 years of fishing, though he acknowledged that there was more money being made in that earlier period, as evidenced by the number of new boats built, and that it was 'easier held on tae then'.

It was his opinion that the most successful ring-netting partnerships were family-based, usually brother neighbouring brother, and cited the McDougalls and Jacksons of Tarbert and the McCrindles and Sloans of Maidens as proof. Brothers, he believed, 'got on better' one with another, but there had to be a 'leader', and if one of the partners – not necessarily the better fisherman – was allowed to make the vital decisions, the partnership was likely to prosper.

Good crews were essential too. 'Everybody knew their job an they wir aw very professional, an that's how they could work in poorer weather. A ring-net wis only as effective as the crew that wir haulin it. The way it wis hauled made an awfu difference tae what it caught.' During his years with the Sloans, there were remarkably few crew-changes. In fact, there was a 'waitin-list' for berths in the boats. 'It used tae be if ye saw somebody walkin along the quay, ye knew what boat wis in the harbour. Ye know, ye jeest connected certain men wi certain boats, but ye wouldnae know now fae day tae day what boats they're on.' [Hugh McPhee]

'Greed'

To Hugh McPhee's question, 'What's the difference between a fisherman and a good fisherman?' his own answer was: 'Greed.' He'd perhaps be the first to agree that the definition is a simplified one, but here is his rationale: 'The one that catches the most is gonny end up the best fisherman, isn't he? And make the most money.' With a good ring of herring, early on in the night, the average skipper would be content to get away in first to market; but not the 'special case' – he wouldn't be satisfied until he'd filled both boats to the gunnels. Come Friday, the average skipper would reason, 'Oh, we've a good week – we'll go away home'; but not the other fellow – he'd 'stick it out tae the bitter end.'

One night the *Wistaria* was leaving Barra Sound and came up on the Jackson pair from Tarbert. 'Jackson's got a big fishin the night,' Billy Sloan remarked. 'Us goin away wi the two boats full,' Hugh laughed. 'He wisnae even content when he had the fou o the two boats!' It was the practice aboard the *Wistaria* that, after the boat had been loaded, a last brailerful of herring would be poured over the deck. Half-an-hour later, when the contents of the hold had settled, these herring – 30 or 40 baskets – would be scooped off the deck and into the hold to top up the cargo and 'fill every corner' before the hatches were battened down. [Hugh McPhee]

In the bights

When two boats come together to close the ring of the net and combine the crews for hauling – 'meeting the boats', in the fishermen's phraseology – the crews would be chapping the anchor or splashing the fending-off poles to scare the herring into the back of the net. When the electric light came into use, the flashing of the outriggers served the same purpose. But in the North, when shot in a bight, it was sometimes wiser to disturb the herring as little as possible, and the cry to the neighbour-boat would be: 'Don't flash yer lights!' The herring were so thickly massed, the fishermen were afraid that when the shoal came off, it would 'flatten the net'. The gear would go 'straight up an doon' and in all like-lihood the net would burst. At other times, though, the net-boat's crew would ask the neighbouring crew to train the searchlight on the beach and then the herring might be seen jumping out of the water as they were coming off the shore. In the North, however, a ring-net would practi-cally fill a small bight and hem in the herring. 'A mean,' Andy Alexander reasoned, 'both boats wir rubbin thir bows against the rocks … They could hardly escape ye.' [Andy Alexander]

'Intae the grass …'

'I cou'na get close enough in – intae the grass,' Neil Jackson remarked. 'Ye never forgot,' he said. If he shot in a particular spot and the net 'ran' there – ie, came in without meeting any obstruction on the bottom – then that was in his 'computer', he said, tapping his head. He knew exactly where he was and would store the knowledge for the future. It was, he said, extraordinary how often the boats could be filled at that time. He estimated that out of 20 rings, the boats would be filled with 19 of them, so thick were the herring. He liked to be hunting down the shore ahead of other boats, but there were times when that was impossible and he'd be 'on a fella's stern', and get herring that the other crew had failed to notice. 'They must've been wonderin how they wir passin them an they wirna twiggin. They wirna goin in. They wirna goin in far enough.'

Neil recited the Jacksons' customary haunts, including Eriskay, espe-cially in a bight on the north side of the island, inside where the *Politician* grounded (p 177). If the herring were in at all, they'd be in that bight. One shot and the boats were away loaded. And if they weren't in that bight, they might be in the next one, at the mouth of the harbour; but that was a difficult bight to shot in because there is a very hard bit of ground out where the end of the net would be dropped. The trick was to shoot on the north side of the ground, and when the neighbour-boat would catch the end he would trail it away clear.

It took the Eriskay ring-net men a long time to master that haul and they tore plenty of nets in the process. Neil Jackson never tired of telling them to keep in. Calum MacKinnon, the leading skipper out of Eriskay, would say to Neil every now and again: 'I can't get that shot at the mouth of the harbour.' – 'Ye'll need tae wait till ye see me in it, actually,' Neil advised him. 'Then come right close in an study.' Neil imagined nights when the Eriskaymen would be watching, from their windows, the ringers at the mouth of their harbour, and saying: 'There's these Jacksons again going away loaded with herring.' Neil Jackson: 'They got it eventually. An, by God, Calum wis a good fisherman wance he did get it.' [Neil Jackson]

Blowing the net out

In a lot of places, if the net failed to encircle or to contain herring, it would tear, because the ground was hard; but if the skipper got the net around herring, then the herring might keep the net off the bottom. The fish were often so thick that they 'blew the net oot [and] it never got time tae settle on the bottom'. Fishermen didn't have to 'see much' when they were searching tight in to the land. At the Bight of the Duff, on the north end of Skiport Bay, if a single 'stroke' was seen on the echo-meter, 'the herrin wis plestered up on the rocks'. [Robert Ross]

Two ticks on the meter

The *Hercules* – neighbouring the *Heritage* – was steaming out through Pabbay Sound, her skipper, Hugh Edgar, checking a chart in the wheelhouse and his cousin 'Dobbin' Gibson stationed on the bow looking for a big rock that they expected to find at the mouth of Sandray Sound. It was spotted just as they were nearly abeam of it. A little later, on the north side of Sandray itself, two tiny ticks, 'a net-length apairt', were seen on the echo-meter. These had earlier been commented on by Bert Andrew of the *Pathfinder*, talking over the radio to his neighbour in the *May Queen*; but they'd passed them by. Hugh, however, decided to investigate the marks, which prompted his cousin to complain: 'Whit ir ye daein?' – 'A'm jeest wonderin,' Hugh replied, 'if there aucht in atween them.' Eight times he turned on the two ticks before taking the decision to shoot. He shot, in eight fathoms of water, to haul towards the beach, but the north-easterly breeze was 'fresh' inshore, so the catch – 230 cran – was brailed with the boat lying to an anchor. [Hugh Edgar]

Refusal to come off

A ring in Billy's Bight in the middle of the day. The net was shot towards the shore and the two boats drew it right in until the boats themselves were up against the rocks. The herring were between the boats, but wouldn't budge, though the fishermen were 'batterin lik hell wi the skid-doags.' The wind was blowing in on the land and had driven spots of plankton inshore. The herring were feeding on the plankton and continued to feed regardless of what the fishermen did to scare them out into the net. In the end, there was nothing for it but to give up and boat the net. 'Ye could see them wi their backs in the watter,' Denis Meenan recalled. 'It wis that dashed annoyin!' [Denis Meenan]

Tearings

When Jock Meenan retired from the sea, the partnership began to damage nets more frequently. In the elder skipper's absence, there was 'no steadying hand'. Years after ring-netting ended in the North, Denis was back in his old haunts dredging for scallops in the big *Stella Maris III*. He'd prowled up and down that shore in pitch-dark in the middle of winter, dodging through rocks, yet when he returned he found that he wouldn't go in broad daylight where he used to go at night. 'A'd lost the bottle,' he admitted. 'Too ould!' [Denis Meenan]

Along rock faces

The boats would be 'right in along rock faces brailin', where the water was deep enough, Joe Brown recalled. The seas would be surging in at the foot of the cliffs, and only the backwash saving the boats from damage or destruction; the crews would be brailing and watching the shoreline with the Aldis lamp, tension rising by the minute. 'Aye, we're gettin close noo, too close! Watch noo! Hurry up, noo!' Then there would be roars from the men who were keeping watch, and an anxious exchange of words. 'How many's left in the net?' – 'Och, there twinty cran!' – 'Hurry up then! Brail away! We're gettin too close!' With the emptying of the bag, the boats would head off into safer waters. Occasionally, when brailing on a dangerous coast, an anchor would be dropped to hold the boats at a safe distance offshore. [Joe Brown]

Tide in Pabbay Sound

The Jacksons were in Pabbay Sound one night and Neil in the *Village Belle* hauled below a cliff. There was a netful of herring, dried up perfectly, but Neil had misjudged the tide, and his brother, Willie the 'Count', was shouting to him: 'Ye'll need tae waatch oot!' The *Village Belle* was being swept 'the wrong way' through the Sound and around the back of the island, where a 'skair', or reef, lies. Neil was none the less determined to hang on to the bagful of herring and asked his brother to come and assist, but Willie was seeing the broken water all around the net-boat and refused. 'Let the bloody herrin go,' he replied. 'A'm no comin roond!' Neil therefore ordered one of his crewmen, Archie Carmichael, to let go the anchor, so Archie went forward and threw it out. Neil actually heard the 'clink' of the anchor, and Archie called to him: 'Heh, Neil – this anchor's hit the ground afore it's right oot ma hand!' – 'Aye, right, boys,' Neil ordered, 'everybody hold on tae the centre o the net an jist let them go.' So the herring were spilled out of the net, and by the time the anchor was got aboard, there was froth rising all around the boat. She was on top of the skair, in shallow water. 'The tide wis the wrong way, ye see,' Neil explained. 'Instead o sweepin me oot, it swept me in.' [Neil Jackson]

Robert Ross remembered a night there was a big fishing in Pabbay Sound and eight ring-nets were lost with tide and hard ground. Archie Paterson of Carradale had a fright at the mouth of Pabbay Sound in the 1960s. It was his first time in there and he was neighbouring Johnny McMillan in the *Maid of the Mist*. He described the ground there as 'jeest a heckle and peaks every way', but, as in all such cases, a net was shot in the expectation that the sheer bulk of herring would lift it clear of the bad ground. He'd shot on the 'top of the tide' – approaching high-water slack – had a good ring of herring, and both crews were brailing by the time ebb water began.

Another Carradale pair, the *Bairn's Pride* and the *Florentine*, were coming out of the Sound, heading east, and their crews were shouting that they'd lost a net and that there was an island up ahead with skairs about it. Panic ensued and some one said to 'throw away the anchor'. With the wisdom of hindsight, Archie admitted that this was 'the wrong thing tae do', because 'the tide wis that strong that the herrin wir gonny take charge when the anchor brought up'. As it happened, when the

Maid of the Mist's crew were ordered, from the *Harvest Queen*, to cut the back-rope, two of the crew acted at once and the rope was cut simultaneously fore and aft, with the result that the top bag and a part of the lower bag were carried away by the weight of herring; but the two boats were brought round before they went in on top of the reef, on which the buoys of the *Bairn's Pride*'s lost net could be seen. The crews had been able to take about 120 cran out of the net before it parted, and the bags were later recovered by a Mallaig crew and put ashore at Castlebay.

Archie took a bottle of whisky aboard the Mallaig boat by way of reward and he and his crew were able to reassemble the net. The net belonging to Jim Campbell of the *Bairn's Pride* was spotted by the crew of the Irish pair-trawler, *Green Pastures*, west of the Hebrides, and retrieved in a damaged condition. The skipper of the *Florentine*, John McConnachie, recollected that the crews aboard the *Bairn's Pride* had to 'stand clear' when the tide swept the net away, otherwise it would have carried them overboard. [Archie Paterson]

Aground, Hound Sound

There was a Campbeltown crew shooting its net one night in the Hound Sound, on the north side of Eriskay. The men who were aft helping the net out soon realised that it wasn't going out and shouted to the skipper, 'Go aheid!' – 'We canna go aheid!' he shouted back. The boat was high and dry! [Denis Meenan]

Tide in Loch Eynort

The McCrindles of Maidens rang in a bight at the head of Loch Eynort and were about to let go an anchor when the tide got them. The man who let go the anchor couldn't catch the rope, it was running out so fast; the boat was being swept through a gut so rapidly that he couldn't catch the rope to take turns on it and secure it. The boat finished up in the inner loch, and that's where the crew brailed the herring. When they returned to the loch and had a look at low water, they saw, right in the middle of it, a ridge of rocks. 'Wir we naw lucky!' [Angus McCrindle]

Adrift in fog

Two Tarbert boats – Eoghann MacFarlane's *King Fisher* and Dugald Bain's *Silver Birch* – were out one night around Barra when a dense fog descended. It was decided to tie the boats together and lie until the fog lifted, but, when daylight came, the boats were out in the Atlantic west of Barra. A strong tide had swept them out through a sound! [Robert Ross]

Shooting strategies

'We never steamed through a bight full-speed,' Grieve Gemmell emphasised. It was the practice to hasten to where herring were known to be and to slow down before the bight was reached, and then proceed dead-slow through it. He preferred to have a 'look doon the shore' (i.e. search in a southerly direction, so that he could 'ring back' at once on a spot of herring, without having to turn about and maneouvre into a shooting position, thus risking disturbing the spot). If it happened that he was going north along the shore, he'd 'keep off a wee berth' (i.e. keep a bit further offshore than usual, and, then, in the bights where he knew he could ring or where he knew herring were frequenting, go round about and proceed 'back in there canny'). [Grieve Gemmell]

Marking a spot

Frequently, when a bunch of herring was felt on the wire and the boat was 'heading in the wrong direction', the location of the shoal would be marked by a bottle kept handy for dropping over the side. Rather than go through the spot of herring and risk dispersing it, the skipper would 'take jeest a wee berth clear in the cant an then shoot roon aboot that area'. That simple device greatly reduced the risk of the skipper's misjudging the shoal's position under a featureless expanse of water. [Matt Sloan]

Over the side

During the Minch summer fishing one year, the *Moira* and *Rhu-na-Gal* were up from Campbeltown. Mattha Speed in the *Moira* shot on a gannet at the back of the Stac at Canna, and for some reason Tom Speed – Neil in the *Rhu-na-Gal*'s son – went over the side with the middle net-buoy. The crew looked about to see where he was and left him hanging on the buoy. There was no panic – he was 'as safe as houses', paddling at the back of the net and waiting until it would be hauled back aboard. [Iain Gemmell]

One night, the *Britannia* was lying with a ring of herring 'dried up' alongside. Her neighbour, Ian Gibson's *Fairwind*, came 'roon aboot' to start brailing, and her wash caused the *Britannia* to roll heavily. There was an old fellow seated atop the middle buoy, amidships on the *Britannia*, and, as the boat rolled back, the motion pitched both him and the buoy overboard. He swam back to the boat's side, and, as he was being hauled back aboard, one of the boys remarked to him – he always had plenty of money about him – 'Still got yer wallet, McG——?' This mischievous remark started him into a panic of fumbling in his back pocket. [Jim Munro]

Transferring crews

In rough seas, shooting the net was the least of concerns. The main problem often arose when the time came to transfer men on to the net-boat, to assist with the hauling. This involved 'meeting the boats', when the end of the net which the neighbour-crew had picked up and towed was passed back aboard the net-boat and four of the neighbouring crew would jump with it as the two boats met, bow to bow. Four Dunure boats were heading from Muldonich to North Bay to drop anchor on a 'wild nicht', when Mungo Munro, skipper of the *Valhalla*, came on to the radio and asked Grieve Gemmell in the *Storm Drift*, 'Dae ye think we'll manage, Grieve?' – 'Aye,' Grieve replied, and that was them committed. The *Valhalla* shot. The other two boats ran down alongside the *Valhalla* to try to get their men aboard, but out of the eight men that could have got aboard, only one managed it. The *Storm Drift*'s crew was now fully committed. Four men out of her dropped about 20 feet on to the *Valhalla*'s deck, as the *Valhalla* fell on the sea and the *Storm Drift* rose. This was at the back of the Curachan, and the *Girl Margaret* was taken in and loaded. [Iain Gemmell]

A clout, meeting the boats

The *Harvest Hope* – neighbouring the *Star of Hope* – had a ring in the Fairway one night and had to call the *Stella Maris* and *Regina Maris* along-side to assist with boating the net. In the rush to get his crew aboard the *Harvest Hope*, Pat McKay hit her a 'clout' with the *Regina* and split the upper of the longitudinal planks that served as bends. (The *Harvest Hope* wasn't a conventional ringer, but had been built – lightly, at that – as a seine-netter.)

Both pairs were filled before the net burst, and they set off for Mallaig. There was a south-westerly gale blowing outside and, with the roll, the *Harvest Hope* began to leak. Water was seen in the engine-room and the crew began pumping, and continued pumping all the way to Mallaig; but, unknown to anyone, the hold had filled with water. Off Rum, the wind shifted into the south-east, freshening constantly as the *Harvest Hope*, punching her way through rising seas, got heavier and heavier. The propeller was actually out of the water by the time the engine was stopped in Mallaig.

When the hold hatches were lifted off, there wasn't a board to be seen and, as the skipper, James Macdonald, recalled: 'There wasn't wan scale on the herrin.' Notwithstanding the condition of the fish, the buyer on the Klondyker in Loch Nevis was delighted with the 'beautiful clean herring', as he described them. The boat's baskets and scoops were nowhere to be seen in the hold and had to be replaced. These weren't recovered until the catch was almost entirely discharged; they'd gone to the bottom of the hold along with the boards. [James Macdonald]

Pirates

The meeting of boats to transfer a crew is normally a rather tense business, even in the best of weather. Imagine the reaction of the *Hercules'* crew, when, one night in the Minch, the crew of her temporary neighbour, Dunky MacDonald's *Golden Hind*, jumped aboard dressed as pirates and brandishing wooden swords! The Dunure crew's neighbour hadn't got back across to Castlebay from Mallaig that evening, so she was paired with the *Golden Hind* of Campbeltown, which also lacked a neighbour. [Hugh Edgar]

Knowing the Grounds

In the early years of ring-netting in the North, fishermen had to familiarise themselves with fishing grounds that were entirely new to them. Since much of the fishing was done tight to the shore and in creeks and channels and among rocks and reefs, often in powerful tides, the accumulation of a working knowledge of the innumerable hazards that they faced, day and night, was of paramount importance. That knowledge could be gained the hard way, in damage to boats and gear, but the more conscientious of fishermen preferred to explore their new environment at their leisure and in ideal conditions.

Explorations

At the summer fishing in the North, there was minimal darkness and the days were long. On a good day, the fishermen would explore the coast, trying channels here and inlets there. Initially, for example, it was the custom to steer outside of Deer Island, north of Loch Boisdale, but some fishermen would look at the island and think, We could go in through that. Eventually, the channel was tried, found to be navigable and was used thereafter, saving a little time. Further north, the channel between the Stuley islands and the coast of South Uist – the Soon o the Stuleys, to fishermen – was likewise found to be entirely safe and that too became a short-cut. [John McIntyre]

Cautious

'We wir gey cautious – that's the truth tae ye – very cautious. We'd jeest tae feel wir wey.' So said Turner McCrindle of Maidens, recalling his first years ringing in the North, in the early 1930s. 'Of course, we had charts there as well, but there's nothin lik experience tae know where ye are.' Jimmy McCreath of Girvan, wherever he happened to be, would go out in the *May*, at low water and in daylight, to explore the ground, 'an then that wis him – he knew it for the night'. He had a gun and would go shooting, which pursuit took him round the islands. Other crews had reason to be grateful for 'Kruger's' close attention to his surroundings, for in later years he was able to guide them into places he had once studied. [J. Turner McCrindle]

That desire for knowledge persisted among the class of skippers that made their names in the post-war period. During the summer fishing, in May, June and July, if an opportunity arose during the day, Matt Sloan would go into unfamiliar lochs at low tide and cruise around, secure in the knowledge that, if the boat struck on a rock, 'in these circumstances … shortly the tide'll make an ye'll float off'. Uisge Bhagh, however, was a loch he had 'no particular desire tae explore at all, because it's full o rocks'.

He recalled exploring a 'gutter' at the head of MacCormick's Bight in Loch Skiport one day. He took the boat up as far as he could but couldn't turn. He'd to go astern down the inlet for quite a distance before the boat could be turned to steam back out.

The Ayrshiremen generally didn't engage seriously in the North winter-fishing until after the Second World War, and Matt Sloan prepared himself by visiting a chart-supplier in Glasgow and purchasing a large selection of charts, each one 'more or less the plan of one loch. In other words, A had a plan of Loch Skiport, Loch Carnan, Loch Maddy – you name it, the whole lot o them – rather than one chart which embodied the whole lot for perhaps half the length of the Hebrides. We had these charts in detail.' [Matt Sloan]

Kruger's Bights

When the *Watchful* and *Wistaria* were working in a foursome with the McCrindles' *Saffron* and *Sapphire*, Matt Sloan in the *Watchful* shot one night in a small bay on the south side of Gighay, Barra Sound. 'Did ye ever see a net shot here before?' one of the McCrindle brothers asked him, adding. 'The grun's aw bad roond aboot here.' – 'Aye, A know,' Matt replied, 'but A can remember 'Kruger' ringin in here an we wir surprised that his net came.' Matt Sloan's net 'came' too (i.e. was hauled undamaged) on that occasion. The bay became known as Kruger's Bight or Bicht.

There was another Kruger's Bight, however, on the north-west side of the Heisger at Canna. The Sloans were working with Jimmy McCreath there one summer (see below). Gannets were striking continually in the bight and herring could be felt on the 'wire'. The Sloans rung thrice there, hauling into the rocks, but 'never marked a tail', probably owing to the difficulty the tow-boat had in keeping the net-boat out of her own net. Jimmy McCreath went into the bight later, felt herring on the wire and shot; but he set the back of his net as close to the rocks as he could possibly go and hauled it off the shore. He got the herring! As Matt Sloan remarked: 'He jeest did the opposite thing tae what aw the rest o us had been tryin an it came off.' [Matt Sloan]

At the Heisgeir

In the summer of 1934 – the year the *Veronica* was built at Cockenzie – the Sloans fished the Minch with the brothers Jimmy and Jock McCreath of the *May* and *AJJ&T* of Girvan until the new boat was ready to be collected. Most of the fishing was done around Canna and the Heisgeir and some days they were working areas in which they had never before been. They had no echo-sounders at that time, but they had feeling-wires. They knew there was quite a bit of shallow ground to the west and south-west of the Heisgeir, so they had to 'tread pretty carefully for a day or two' until they 'got the lie o the land'. [Matt Sloan]

Bay Bolum

'Aw the different bichts had different wee snags attached tae them,' Ian Gibson remembered. Bay Bolum – on the north side of Loch Eynort – was one of his own specialities when working in a foursome with the Munro brothers, Sandy and Johnny, in the *Fair Morn* and *New Dawn*, and his cousin Billy in the *Britannia*. 'We could take herrin oot that bicht an nane o the rest o them could,' he said, adding that he hadn't revealed the foursome's method until Bob McCutcheon of the *Silver Quest* lubricated his tongue one night in Oban.

The technique was basically this: when the last of the wide wing started going out, as the net was being shot, the 20-fathom bridle-rope on the end of the net would be quickly hauled clear, and the gable – or end – of the net tied up at the ring-net winch. In effect, the net was a continuous wall of netting, eliminating the likelihood of the herring 'gan oot atween the stern o yer boat an the bridle'. The object then was to 'get intae this wee gutter, jeest in among the wrack', an exceedingly tight corner. As he remarked, however, 'different folk had different bits' that they knew particularly well. There was a haul in the north end of Moonlight Bay, and the only other skippers he saw ringing there, forby himself, were Willie Wilson, Angus McCrindle and Neil Jackson. It was a 'durty bit o grun' that only just accommodated a ring-net. [Ian Gibson]

Solid rock in Pabbay Sound

In 1962 or '63, Hugh Edgar took the *Hercules* through a narrow channel, earlier shown to him by Tommy Ralston, on the south side of the Wine Gless. Emerging into the mouth of Pabbay Sound, he soon came into solid herring and shot the net in a tight circle. The echo-sounder was registering four echoes from the seabed, a sure indication of the hardest of ground. His old mentor, Jock 'Churry' Dunlop 'went aff his heid' and warned him: 'Ye'll loas the bloody net here!' But he got away with it, possibly because the encircled shoal chose to rise and thus kept the net off the bottom. Hugh was in a foursome at the time with three Campbeltown boats, the *Nobles Again*, *Stella Maris* and *Regina Maris*. It was the skipper of the last-mentioned, Pat McKay – an older man that Hugh liked and respected – who picked up the end of the net, and who later remarked to him: 'A've never seen anybody gettin a ring there afore. The only thing A've ever seen them gettin wis doins [bad tearings].' Pat was 'fair ta'en on' with this daring – or reckless – shot, which netted 500-plus cran, so, as Hugh joked, 'A wis his hero for a day or twa, until A blotted ma copybook, nae doot.' [Hugh Edgar]

'Churry'

At this stage, the question might be asked: how did a ring-net skipper acquire his knowledge? Much of that knowledge was gained, to be sure, by trial and error and resultant damage to boats and gear; but the advisory role of older fishermen was another vital factor. Sometimes the support was paternal, but the father-son relationship at fishing was often one fraught with unreasonable expectations, on the one side, and youthful impatience on the other. Hugh Edgar's mentor was an old crew-member, Jock 'Churry' Dunlop, who was born in 1900 and fished until the age of 63. Hugh was a boy of nine, spending holidays at sea, when he first encountered him. He addressed him then as 'Mister Dunlap'. Ten years later – at a remarkably early age – he was Jock Dunlop's skipper.

When Hugh joined the crew of his father's *Hercules*, on 15 July 1955, he was to learn a great deal from old 'Churry', with whom he regularly stood watch. He was taught to identify lights and places and trained in compass work. Going through the Sound of Mull, there were no fewer than 11 successive courses to follow, and the first time Hugh looked over his shoulder and allowed the boat's head to deviate from the given course, 'Churry' dealt him 'a belt on the back o the heid' and advised him: 'Ye've goat tae remember, if ye go a quarter a pint [point] that wey for a saicond or twa, go back the other wey.' The compass magnification aboard the *Hercules* was poor and Hugh admitted that 'tae steer tae a quarter o a pint wis difficult, because ye're talkin aboot less than three degrees'.

When Hugh would be in the forecastle, stealing half-an-hour's sleep on the locker, 'Churry' would shout down at him: 'Get up on the deck, ya lazy wee bastard – some day you'll be the only body that kens whaur ye ir!' Within a few years, the prediction was virtually fulfilled. 'For aboot ten years,' Hugh admitted, 'A thought he wis an auld bastard, an then A began tae realise jeest what an asset he had been tae me. He taught me onythin A knew aboot the Minch.' [Hugh Edgar]

Guided

On occasion, the Clyde men took advantage of the Minch fishermen's better knowledge of certain localities, as when, just before Christmas of 1956, the Mansons, in the *Margaret Ann* and *Jessie Alice*, led the *Storm Drift*, *Summer Rose*, *Hercules* and *Britannia* 'in single-file' into the upper part of Loch Eport at low water through masses of rocks and little islands. The herring were 'as thick as the water wis deep', but with the first shot the

Summer Rose's net was torn in pieces. The *Britannia* shot next and rang sufficient herring to fill the four boats. The Manson boats were lying brailing, one of the boats six feet out of the water, hard aground; but the Mallaig men were apparently 'used tae that ... they wir never aff the rocks in there'. The boats left Loch Eport that night at high tide and it was 'a different world' – the guts and channels they'd negotiated at low water had disappeared beneath the surface. When the boats emerged from the loch, there was a lot of southerly wind, so instead of crossing to Mallaig by a southerly course, they went 'north about, round Skye'. [Iain Gemmell]

Loch Uisge Bhagh

'This incident also involved Jim Manson. Jim had the *Margaret Ann* new then. The place was Loch Uisge Bhagh, Kallin. As usual we were looking down by Wiay Island and further north. But apart from the odd gannet diving, nothing on the Kelvin Hughes echo sounder. It was close to this place Uisge Bagh that we saw a lot of gulls among the islands inside. But how to get in there? It was Dunky Donnell [MacDonald], the *Golden Hind*, who found a narrow channel, and he said, 'If you want to, follow me'. There were six pairs of boats, including us and our neighbour, Duncan 'Porter' Gillies in the *Mallaig Mhor*. The rest were Campbeltown and Ayrshire, the Gemmells' *Storm Drift* and *Summer Rose*. Porter shouts to Dunky on the *Golden Hind*, 'Is there much water there?' Dunky shouts back, 'There's nae fuckin water here,' which caused a bit of a laugh. It was something to be remembered.

'From the start the boats were touching bottom. Once through the narrow channel, the area widened out into small bays and such countless small islands. All of Manson's boats from Mallaig were in there and, by the looks of them, loaded with herring. One pair, the *Golden Ray*, and partner, *Mary Manson*, were brailing fish. One was afloat, the other was not – she was on a sandbank. Anyway, boats were ringing away, but one had very little room. Porter hit a boulder while setting the net but jumped off. Out of that ring we got 120 cran.

'The reason you could not mark the herring was, the shoals were spreading out when the boats approached; also, the lack of water. The tide was on the ebb. Not one of the boats had more than two fathom under the keel ... I don't think I ever saw anything like what I saw in that place that day. You could see red rivers of herring coming out from between the rocks and small islands. The gulls were picking them up. This was the herring coming out with the tide. So we now had to wait till the flood tide, as we were well down with 120 cran. All of the boats got a cargo. After we got out, it was blowing a south-easterly gale. Norman [MacInnes], the skipper, decided to make for Gairloch instead of beating against the wind to Mallaig. After a stormy passage of nearly eight hours we made it OK and got £12 a cran. Well, we did not get back to Uisge Bagh any more. The next night we got herring in Corodale. A lot safer Corodale was.' [Duncan MacInnes, letter]

Through the Sound of Harris

'In Stornoway, over the week-end (p. 115), our skipper Mattha had been chatting on and off to the crews of the Scalpay boats and they mentioned to him that they'd be leaving Stornoway early on Monday to sail through the Sound of Harris and chance their luck, weather permitting, along the exposed Atlantic coast of Harris, in the Sound of Taransay and in West Loch Tarbert.

'The course through the Sound, with its many low-lying islets, was not considered to be a recognised channel and was only navigable with local knowledge. It was a perched sound with no aids to navigation except the odd metal rod, sticking up from underwater hazards, and wooden poles set up on islands. Even with local know-how it still had to be negotiated during daylight hours. One of the Scalpay skippers made the remark that our pair of boats were much faster than their two, so Mattha deduced he was perhaps suggesting that we follow them through.

'That is what transpired. We eventually rounded Toe Point and set course for Taransay Island, the echo-sounder indicating a bottom of pure sand. All three pairs of boats had big shots. Our last haul, as dawn was breaking, was opposite the old whaling factory at Bunaveneadar at the head of West Loch Tarbert. The factory was started by Norwegians over 100 years ago. All that remains is the concrete floor pad and the distinct landmark of the tall brick chimney standing. We navigated back through the Sound of Harris without incident and arrived in Gairloch around dinnertime on Tuesday. *Acacia* had 152 cran of herring on board and *Westering Home* 35 cran (748 baskets). Before we could start to discharge, we had hours to wait on transport arriving from South Shields. To my knowledge, no Clyde-based fishing boats ever ventured back through the Sound of Harris. I wonder why not.' [Duncan Ritchie, letter]

'One of my first trips to the North in 1950 had us through the Sound of Harris with the *Morag Bhan*. We didn't get much there, but the passage through the Sound was unforgettable. You steamed in for a wee island just off Leverburgh, then turned and went straight for the shore. There were leading marks there, and you had to go right in close to the shore before turning to port and heading west. There was the wreck of an Admiralty trawler lying just on the shore there – he had gone too close! She was bottom-up and when the tide was coming, there was a spout of water driven up through a hole, maybe a seacock, in her bottom. It was like the spout of a whale!

'When we were in that area we used to lie in Rodel, in a beautiful wee harbour there; you dried out in it. You could phone the Co-operative in Stornoway with a store list, and they would send it down on the bus ... The hotel was visited by the Royal family later, and as a result, they were granted a licence to sell 'Royal Household' whisky. I went there last year [1999] to discover the hotel derelict.' [Tommy Ralston, letter]

The feeling-wire

That fish-detection instrument, which came into vogue in the early 1930s, comprised up to 100 fathoms (182m) of lead-weighted fine wire or twine, wound on to the end of a fish-box. There were men who could operate the wire sensitively and therefore effectively, and others who couldn't.

A Dunure skipper, Johnny Munro, employed the feeling-wire to increase his knowledge of the sea-bottom. One of the crew would stand on the port shoulder of the boat with the taut wire trailing astern, feeling for herring touching on it. The theory was that, by standing forward, any herring close to the surface would be 'shedding off the boat' and might be felt, whereas, if the wire-man was positioned aft, he probably wouldn't feel any at all. On a bitterly cold winter's night, the wire-man's job was hardly covetable, and while the wire-man was sounding, the skipper would be asking, 'What's the bottom feel like?' If the lead was 'giving a chug', then that might be a 'fool', or foul, bottom. In that way, the skipper got to know the nature of the ground that lay, unseen, beneath the keel. When, in the post-war period, echo-sounders became standard equipment on fishing-boats, the degree of shading on the meter-paper would indicate if the bottom was hard or soft. 'But by that time, of course,' Johnny Munro added, 'we more or less kent where we could really go, up North there, wi any freedom.' [Johnny Munro]

In the North, fishing was almost always along the shore. Aboard the *Margaret Rose*, Jack Galbraith and James McKinven were wire-men most of the time. In the matter of ground-awareness, Archie Graham considered echo-sounding to be less reliable than wiring, because 'it had a spread, and if you were tight in along the land, even although the boat was on good ground, you picked up the hard echo of the rocks or the cliff face'. His crew 'depended very much on going back to feeling the nature of the ground, unless you had local knowledge and you knew the net would run on that particular spot'. [Archie Graham]

As a fish-detector

Davie McNaughton, as a teenager aboard the *Lily*, was instructed in the skills of the feeling-wire by a veteran Dalintober fisherman, Jock McKinlay. He'd call Davie across and let him feel the varying degrees of vibration – a 'light scatter', a 'heavy scatter', and so on. Jock's advice to Davie was: 'There's only wan man knows hoot that is – the man at the wire. Naebody else knows, so it's up tae yersel whether tae shot on it or naw.' [David McNaughton]

A fine art

Angus McCrindle remarked that, at the finish up, the ring-net fishermen knew the North shores 'lik the back o wir han – definitely'. Once they got in on the shore in darkness, they were fine, but if they strayed too far off – 'feenished!' The 'focus' was lost. They had to keep 'right on the shore', and even when 100 or 50 yards off, they would get 'the shadow' and might be deceived into thinking they were 'against the shore'; but once inside that range, it was the actual shore they were seeing. 'Och, a fine art,' he summed up. [Angus McCrindle]

Radar

The top skippers to some extent lost their eminence when radar arrived in the late 1960s. As well as being invaluable for making passages and landfalls, radar also enabled lesser fishermen to see where the top boats were operating. 'It put everybody on the same footin.' Unlike the populous Clyde coasts, the North was an exceedingly dark place in winter: 'There wis hardly a light to be seen as far as habitation an that goes.' The Sloans were particularly clever at going into 'dark holes' to ring herring, but radar 'made it easier for other folk and helped boats that didn't have such competent crews'. [Hugh McPhee]

Electric Light

Electricity, when it became standard aboard the canoe-sterned ringers that were built in the 1930s, was as far-reaching an innovation at sea as it had been on land. The skiff fishermen had long been accustomed to working with candles and paraffin-oil. The forecastle, or 'den', was illumined by paraffin lamps; the deck was lighted by a crude kettle-like 'flambeau', which gave out a naked flame from burning tow compressed into the spout, and the 'winky' itself – which was the light marking the end of the net that the neighbour boat would retrieve – was a buoyed canister with tiny windows through which the light of a candle would glow. Navigation lights were virtually unknown until the 1920s. Before then, it was customary to operate at night without lights of any description.

With the introduction of electricity, fishing boats were able to carry all the required navigation lights. Electricity also revolutionised fishing practices. By training a powerful lamp over the bow, fishermen could see herring swimming close to the surface ahead of the boat. Searchlights could also be used as to scan the shoreline, identifying both locality and potential hazards, and to startle herring out off the shorehead and into the net; and while the net was being hauled, a flashing light – usually the 'outrigger', which was attached to a spar on the port side of the wheelhouse, and could be swung outboard when light was required on deck or over the side – served to keep herring in the net until the soles were closed, thus trapping the shoal.

Dimming the outrigger

Some crews, when working on deck – perhaps hauling the net back on to the stern in readiness for the next shot – would throw a bag over the outrigger to reduce its brightness, especially when steaming along the shore, for bright lights disturbed herring. [Neil Jackson]

The 'Ghosts'

The McDougalls of Tarbert were famous for their aversion from light, and used dimmers on board the boats. This practice made the boats difficult to see on the shore and earned the McDougalls the nick-name of 'the Ghosts'. 'The first thing ye wid see,' Iain Gemmell recalled, 'wid be a wee peep o licht an that wid be them appearin.' Robert Ross remarked that 'ye wid need a light tae look for the lights'. The McDougall crews were kitted out with black oilskins, 'so that they wouldn't shine'. This preoccupation with muted lighting wasn't, however, entirely about working in secrecy; it was also about minimising disturbance of herring.

'Corodale was Matt Sloan's hunting ground. Also the McDougalls of Tarbert, *Fionnaghal* and *Mairearad*. One could be cruising round this coast from Loch Eynort to Loch Skiport without a mark on the sounder. After about one or two in the morning one went for a sleep, usually in Loch Skiport. Next day, the herring news from Mallaig was that the McDougalls, or the 'Ghosts', as they were called, would be in with full boats. This miracle was quite common with the Sloans as well. How did they do it? It seems the herring sometimes were so close to the shore, the bold boys put searchlights on the cliff after shooting the net. It always pulls off the herring. The herring took off, with the light on the shore, into the net. But, be that as it may, the McDougalls were uncanny.

'When we discovered about the light on the cliffs things improved. One night in Telegraph Bay, south of Brevig on Barra, we tried that trick again with the *Mallaig Mhor*, and as soon as we started hauling we knew we had more than enough. After we got the soles up, the herring could be seen pouring over the corks. The corks were straight up and down. There were three men on each end of the net that night but it was not till a lot of fish left the net we made it. We got the full of both boats, 300 cran, and off to Mallaig early – 9 o'clock. That made a difference, as one got a couple of hours sleep before the bell and the herring sales. Also, the steam across was three hours to the Isle of Canna and three hours from there to Mallaig; three men in a watch, so that was another three hours one got below.' [Duncan MacInnes, letter]

Shooting the net

Some pairs of ringers, in the post-war period, carried identification lights on the stern, which facilitated mutual recognition. This was a matter of particular importance when herring had been located and the net was about to be shot. If the neighbouring crew was oblivious to the net's going out and didn't appear to catch and tow the end, the whole operation would be rendered futile. That, however, was a very rare occurence.

One of the crew – usually the boy – was always detailed to watch the neighbour-boat, and in particular for his winky 'going away'. His position was usually aft, lying on top of the net. The skipper too would be alert, and Neil Jackson recalled that even when working among 'therty boats in a heap', he could look all around and pick out his neighbour without actually having been following the boat's movements. In the North, however, boats tended to work a great deal of the time in isolation, keeping to their own well-tried haunts. On very rare occasions a pair of boats would shoot simultaneously.

As soon as a skipper decided to shoot, he would switch on the distinctively coloured 'winch-light', at the fore end of the wheelhouse. That was the initial signal of his intention, but would often be reinforced by a more emphatic signal.

Recognition

The neighbour boat had to be watched at all times throughout the night to see which way he was turning or when he was going to shoot. If visual contact were lost, then – in the latter years – a call on the radio would elict a flash of light, by which the missing boat's position would be revealed. Some pairs of boats carried identification lights which were peculiar to themselves and which simplified the maintenance of contact, particularly when working among a concentration of other boats. The *Stella Maris* and *Regina Maris* of Campbeltown each had a blue all-round light and, below that, a white forward-shining light, on their mizzen mast, while the *Saffron* and *Investors* of Maidens, instead of the normal small dim stern light at the back of the wheelhouse, had two lights, one above the other, a foot or so apart. The Sloans boats' signal to each other was the letter 'V', flashed in Morse Code – three shorts and a long – using a searchlight or the side-lights on the wheelhouse or whatever. That 'V' represented the name *Veronica*, which was one of the Sloan boats in the 1930s. {Iain Gemmell, Matt Sloan]

Searchlights

If a ring-netter shot in a bay, once the net was towed in so far, the crew would begin flashing a light into the shore-head. The first light in use was the powerful 'Aldis' lamp, which the Royal Navy employed for signalling. The purpose of the flashing light was to scare the herring off the shore and into the net. 'Ye flashed them aff intae the net,' as Grieve Gemmell put it, adding: 'Sometimes ye flashed too bloody many aff!' He remembered going into some of the lochs in the North and training the 'Aldis' lamp overboard, 'an ye could see them soomin lik buggary … It wis a great sicht sometimes.' Other times, going into a bight and switching on the light, the herring would rise in a solid mass 'as high as the boat.' They were, he said, 'jeest packed in, an they jeest rose up richt oot the watter'. [Grieve Gemmell]

The searchlight, manned on the bow, was also used for picking out points of land and for illumining the shore itself as the boat progressed along. Prolonged use of the searchlight tended to disturb herring in the bights, hence the fishermen's preference for having the shore always on the starboard side when looking for herring. This meant that 'one pass through the bight' was sufficient before turning around and shooting back across the shoal. After the net was shot, the light could be 'applied on to shore tae spring the herrin off intae the net from inside ye. Sometimes it wis a sight tae behold as they rose out the water'. During net-hauling, it might be necessary to flash lights on the deck to keep the herring at the back of the net until the sole closed and trapped the shoal. Not until the net was closed would the deck lights be left on, in order that the men could see what was happening, as the operation reached its climax, and see whether the net was torn. [Iain Gemmell]

Herring rising out of the water

Iain Gemmell recalled one trip the *Storm Drift* made to the North, neighbouring Willie Anderson's *Prospector*, in the mid-1960s. They had returned across the Minch from Oban and were entering Loch Boisdale. The steamers and the fishing fleet were in, so they decided to drop anchor at the back of the island to avoid the congestion. When the searchlight was switched on to let them see where they were going, 'the herrin rose oot the water lik a cloud'. They shot the net and took 80 cran out of it, and the rest of the fleet, lying at the pier, thought they were at anchor. The *Prospector* went away back to Oban with the catch. Unknown to the *Storm Drift*'s crew, the *Prospector* had 'one hellish passage', the wind having freshened from the south-east. [Iain Gemmell]

Cecil Finn saw herring rise out of the water and fall again, against the cliff in Telegraph Bay, when searchlights were directed on to the shore. 'They got the fright wi the light,' he said, 'an the scales wis on the watter wi them; they left the scales.'

Denis Meenan recalled steaming out of Loch Boisdale, both boats loaded with herring got in South Boisdale. All the lights were on as the crew hauled the net aft, and there the herring were, a green mass of them, swimming along with the lights, keeping up with the boat.

Herring following light

The *Wistaria* had left Corodale one night to go to Mallaig, and her neighbour, the *Watchful*, was steaming up between Uisnish Light and the mouth of Loch Skiport. The crew was laying the net – hauling it forward into two or three mounds – when suddenly a spot of herring was seen swimming alongside the brightly-lit boat. One of the crew, Johnny Gibson, lifted a draw-bucket and began dipping it over the side – in the way one would lift water – thinking he would catch a herring in it. He tried several times without success, whereupon the skipper, Matt Sloan, left the wheelhouse and said to him, 'Let me see the bucket, Johnny'. Matt dropped the bucket the reverse way. Instead of angling the mouth of it in the direction in which the boat was travelling, he dropped the bucket with the mouth facing aft, and by the time it hit the water, the snap of the bucket had turned it the opposite way. With three drops, Matt caught 19 herring from the shoal that was swimming alongside.

When the *Watchful* entered Loch Skiport there was a pair of 'Auchies' lying there. When Matt got alongside them, he told the crews: 'Aboot half-way between the mooth o the loch here an directly doon fae Uisnish Light, there's a spot o herrin oot there, because – look – there they are.' The herring were still flapping on the deck, but the Avoch crews were disinclined to believe him. 'Noo, look here,' he said, 'how could these herrin be alive? There's the net lyin forrid on the boat. There's the herrin lyin kickin on the boat.' One of the Avoch skippers asked Matt where he had come from. 'We've come up from Corodale,' he replied. 'Oor neebor's away tae Mallaig.' Explaining further, he added: 'We had the lights on workin wi the net, the ootriggers, an these herrin wir actually swimmin alongside us.' – 'Ah,' said the 'Auchie', 'ye're havin us on!' – 'A'm no,' Matt protested, 'A'm tellin ye the truth!' They would hardly believe him, but they did go out. He couldn't remember whether or not they got a fishing; perhaps they failed to locate the spot. [Matt Sloan]

Missing the shooting signal

'To land their catch of herring, one of the pair of boats would cross the Minch to the market port, the other boat remaining in the area of the fishing grounds awaiting the neighbour's return. Frequently in the winter months, gales would start to blow and the fishing boat returning from market, battling its way west, would have to take refuge in the small sheltered harbour on the Isle of Canna. Sometimes Canna harbour would be jam-packed with ring-net boats at anchor. With a sudden easing of the gale, and with the use of radio, the boats would agree to pair up with another pair of boats.

'One time our boat, the *Acacia*, was in this particular situation, and we paired up with the renowned Tarbert fisherman, Tommy Jackson. Both crews had every intention of returning home for the following week-end.

We left Canna in company with Jackson and headed for the Heisgeir, the remote low rocky island with the tall lighthouse, south of Canna. The other boats that were sheltering headed away west across the Minch.

'During the night, we were constantly in touch by radio with our neighbour-boats across the Minch. Both our boats went back and forth with the echo-sounder continually pinging away and the wire out. This went on for hours, with not a tap felt. We learned that there was nothing doing where our neighbours were fishing, so it was agreed that they should leave the area and join us. Then we would all set course for the Crinan Canal, moor the boats in the Canal Basin and go home for a long week-end.

'With the monotony of sailing continually back and forth over the same course and coming upon no sign of herring whatsoever, our skipper suggested that the cook make tea. When it was ready, the cook took over from the skipper at the wheel with one other crew member out on deck. At this particular time, we were out of sight of Jackson's boat. We really thought Jackson was in the same frame of mind as we were, that being, just to kill time until the other boats' navigation lights could be sighted. We learned there and then that that is not how Jackson's keen fisherman's mind worked. It is, when at sea, continually concentrating on seeking for herring – an indisputable sign of an exceptional fisherman.

'Anyway, when we caught sight of his boat's light it was panic stations with us. We immediately realised he had his net shot. His winky was bobbing about quite some distance from his boat, indicating to us that he had been shot for some time prior to us twigging his actions. We lifted the winky light, and from then until the net – containing a big big catch of herring – was dried up, everything went like clockwork.

'Our crew said little after our affront of not keeping a proper watch. We talked earlier that we had all to be on our toes now that we were neighbouring such a celebrated fisherman. The boats were now squared, our crew attending to swinging the brailer pole out in readiness to start brailing the herring into our hold … then disaster! The for'ard brailer pole guy-rope broke, the pole swung aft, coming up with a crash against the wheelhouse, and on its way broke the outrigger light. We then had to set-to, lower the pole and splice on a new guy-rope.

'Tommy said afterwards that it was quite a pantomime to watch and that he really sensed how we felt; also that it had been an ambition of his to fill the *Acacia* to the coamings with herring, and he was quite content to wait and see it happen. We did not radio to the other boats that we had a big shot, and they were pleasantly surprised when they arrived to find both boats busy brailing the herring. With our two boats loaded, there was still a lot of herring in the net and that had to be taken on board one of the other boats. To this day the rest of the fishing fleet maintained that we had called our neighbours across the Minch, so as they could share in the herring that we had located earlier on. This was not the actual situation. All four boats left the Heisgeir on course for Ardnamurchan and the Sound of Mull to sell and discharge our big catch at Oban.' [Duncan Ritchie, letter]

Big Shots
· · · · · · · · · · · · ·

A 'shot' was a catch, and the bigger the better as far as fishermen were concerned.

Bay Harty

The Jacksons were going down through Bay Harty and Calum MacKinnon, the Eriskay skipper, shouted them alongside. He had five boats there, yet he summoned the two Tarbert crews alongside, a testimony to their sound reputation. Neil Jackson went in with his crew, caught the middle net-buoy and strapped the *Village Belle* to the bag of the net. Then Willie, his brother, came in with the smaller *Village Maid* and she too was strapped to the bag. Finally, an Eriskay boat also came in: four boats around the bag of the net. Neil Jackson was astonished at the degree of abuse the knotless nylon bag was taking, both from the strain the tow-boat was exerting and from the weight of the four boats lashed to it, and he said to his brother: 'Christ, we'll need tae get wan o they bags'. Once the four boats were filled, Neil remarked: 'What's he gonny do noo?'

MacKinnon soon demonstrated his strategy for releasing the loaded boats without jeopardising the catch remaining in the bag of the net. He left his brailing-pole out, let the two outside boats go, pulled the *Village Belle* in, tied the lashing of his brailer-wire on to the middle of the bag, and then got the Tarbert crew to cut their lashings, thus leaving the bag hanging on his brailing-pole. When Neil next looked, the Eriskaymen had the brailer-wire on the winch and had heaved the bag well up, so that the other crew coming in had no difficulty lashing on to it. Then they gathered the slack netting in the middle, lashed it too and heaved it up on the winch, which was then stopped. The second boat came round and she too was lashed to the bag, after which they shouted to the fellow in the tow-boat to go ahead. All the herring in that net were secured. It was about the biggest ring of herring Neil Jackson ever saw, a 'colossal bag'. The two Tarbert boats had 400 cran between them and all seven boats went away for market loaded. Neil Jackson saw Calum MacKinnon excel another night, in the Wine Gless, when the net yielded 800 cran. [Neil Jackson]

Out of land

The Jacksons left Loch Boisdale one January night and headed north, only to meet a big fleet of boats coming down, which meant only one thing – there was nothing doing. So, the brothers canted and went away south and reached Barra Sound without seeing any sign of herring. By that time, they were hearing the other skippers speaking on the radio, heading away for the Crinan Canal and home. The Tarbertmen had continued two or three more miles south, when Willie called Neil on the radio: 'Where the hell are ye goin? How far doon are ye goin?' – 'A'm goin till A run oot o bloody land!' Neil replied. The wind was north-westerly, and strong when the showers would come, but easing afterwards. They searched the whole shore until they reached Mingulay. Down along the white beach and by the 'wee gut' they went, until they were off the lighthouse jetty … and there the herring were!

Neil shot and got the full of the net, which, as was the Jackson practice, was immediately split and part-emptied (p 78). They then proceeded to fill the boats and head away for market. Neil had seen a big drifter going south in the evening but hadn't seen her return and reckoned that 'there somethin doon there when she's no comin up'. That drifter was lying outside the Jacksons, and her skipper spoke to them on the radio, commenting on the time it took to shoot the net, take the herring aboard and be under way. 'Youse'll be in Oban, well in Oban, afore we get the nets lifted,' the skipper concluded. The other ring-net skippers – off Ardnamurchan and heading through the Sound of Mull, empty – couldn't believe what they were hearing when the Jacksons came on the radio with news of their success. 'An there we wir, comin in lodded,' Neil said. 'It jeest shows ye – well, yer determination, but yet yer luck had tae be in. That wis the last land – there wis no further A could go than the slip, an there the herrin wir. An what told me tae go doon there?' [Neil Jackson]

Shepherd's Bay

The MacDougalls of Tarbert had a 'braw touch' in Shepherd's Bay in October 1951. It was the week Archie 'Meekie' Carmichael was married, and Robert Ross – his best man – wasn't on that trip. There was nothing doing on the North Shore – from Loch Boisdale to Loch Skiport – and the two crews went into Shepherd's Bay to lie. The noise of the anchor-chain running out must have disturbed a spot of herring that was lying in the bay, for when the neighbour-boat went in to tie alongside the anchored vessel, the herring were 'playing dry' inside. They shot right away and hauled a couple of hundred cran, which sold at £10 a cran, the first time the crews ever realised that price. Their trip was made. Two thousand pounds, divided by nine shares per boat: six shares to each crew and three to each boat, less expenses. A hundred pounds-plus to each man for a few hours' work. Big money in 1951. [Robert Ross]

Gott Bay

Joe Brown could put an exact date, as to day and month, on this memory. He remembered the date as the fifth of November, because that was Jim Meenan's birthday, and Jim said, 'A never got herrin on ma birthday ever in ma life'. It was in Gott Bay, Tiree, and there were only two pairs there, the *Star of Hope* and *Harvest Hope* and the *Regina Maris* and *Stella Maris*. They left Scarinish in the afternoon and Malcolm McGougan in the *Harvest Hope* was first to shoot, but he effectively missed the spot of herring and ended up with just a scatter of baskets. Next, the Meenans saw a spot, shot and got 'a hell of a ring'. They had to shout the other crews to come and give a hand. Three boats were filled – roughly 150 cran in each – and not only that, a mass of herring was lost through a rip in the net. [Joe Brown]

Eriskay

The 'best ring' Robert McGown ever saw, at the end of a lifetime of fishing, was in the middle of the day at Eriskay around 1961. Five boats were filled from that ring, the *Mary McLean*, *Boy Danny*, *Golden Hind* and 'two North boats'. They had been going out 'in the first o the night', but finding little doing, so they decided to take a turn out early one day. Going 'up along the back o Eriskay', they saw a gannet circling. The fish-ermen knew by the way a gannet circles and circles that it must be on a spot of herring. As Robert said, 'It must just be waitin tae get the edge o the herrin'. Down went the gannet. Both the *Golden Hind* and the *Boy Danny* went for the spot, but the *Golden Hind* took it. Each of the five boats took 150 or 160 cran aboard and there was a lot of herring let go after the boats were loaded. The *Boy Danny*, aboard which Robert was fishing, had her decks as well as hold full of herring. [Robert McGown]

Loch Shell

This follows on from the shooting incident recorded on p 13.

Loch Shell was full of herring. The *Storm Drift II* was neighbouring the *Summer Rose*, the *Hope* and the *Good Design* at the time. Going up the loch, Sammy Gemmell, in the wheelhouse of the *Storm Drift*, slowed her down, the feeling-wire was unwound … and wouldn't go down through the herring, so densely-packed was the shoal. Gulls appeared on the scene and began swooping and picking herring out of the water, in broad daylight. The *Storm Drift*'s net was shot, and when the soles came up, the herring were 'solid dry'. Three boats went to the corks to lash up, and they were so far away that the crew of the *Storm Drift* couldn't throw ropes to them. Grieve Gemmell was laughing at all of this, and his father turned to him and said, 'Ye shou'nae be bloody laughin – we'll loas wir net here'. The light lower bag of the net actually did burst, but there was such a bulk of herring that the uppermost fish just couldn't get down; so the crew of the *Storm Drift* hauled along the selvedge until they got to the heavy upper bag, pulled up the edge of it and managed to save 300 cran. As Grieve later reflected, 'God knows whoot wis in that net'. [Grieve Gemmell]

Heisgeir

The *Nobles* and the *Glen Carradale* were 'three boats' with the *Margaret Hamilton*, whose neighbour – the *Falcon* – the *Nobles* had earlier run down in Bay Harty, so that the damaged boat was forced to return home for repairs. The three boats crossed to the Heisgeir. Davie McNaughton was standing with Peter Robertson on the deck of the *Nobles* when Peter exclaimed, 'Look at that big black lump aheid o us – A bate ye that's herrin'. Out with the feeling-wire; went through the spot trailing the wire. 'Oh, in the name o God, A never seen anythin lik yon in ma life!' Davie McNaughton recalled.

They took 'a braider o a shot on them' – a wide sweep of the net – and before they could get the soles aboard, the herring were swimming green out the net; this with the extra crew to handle the net-hauling. Duncan McSporran, the skipper of the *Nobles*, took a calm view of events. 'Jeest let her run tae she comes up hersel. We'll get mair than enough.' The crews hadn't got to the shoulders and the net was blowing away out and the back buoys sinking out of sight. They hauled and hauled and hauled on that net until it burst. In the end, they got 100 cran from that solid lump of herring.

There was such a phenomenal fishing from the Heisgeir that night – boats were coming into market loaded to the gunwales and with fish stowed on the very decks – that the port was closed to landings the following day, so that the catches of that night could be disposed of. 'That', Davie remarked ruefully, 'was the biggest ring ever I saw, an we never got them anyway.' [David McNaughton]

Melvaig Head

Johnny and Sandy Munro filled the *Fair Morn* and *New Dawn* to the hatches in a bight under the sheer face of Melvaig Head. They had been through the bight before, echo-sounding there to check the nature of the ground. Using the minimum of flashing lights, from three hauls they put the remarkable total of 300 cran aboard the *New Dawn* and 200 cran aboard the older *Fair Morn*, which vessel was merely 4 ft (1.22m) shorter. It was the *New Dawn*'s first winter in the Minch and she hadn't been filled until that night. As Johnny Munro remarked, however, 'Ye hadnae much freeboard for any weather. That was the thing ye had tae watch when ye started bargin them down'. [Johnny Munro]

The Fairway

The Carradale pair, *Harvest Queen* and *Maid of the Mist*, went down into the Fairway at Barra one day. The Ayrshire fleet was lying at anchor at the back of Muldonich. There was a gannet circling and looking downward. Archie Paterson in the *Harvest Queen* judged it to be a 'likely gannet', so he passed over where the bird had been looking and saw, on the echo-meter, a mark on the bottom 'like a matchhead', and what he liked about it was, the signal was so strong 'it went right down through the paper'. He decided to shoot the net, and, with that, all the Ayrshire crews got under way and came out.

He'd rung a big spot of herring; 'far too many' he later conceded. The *Harvest Queen* and *Fair Morn* were both filled and then the *New Dawn* came in, but, after 80 cran had been taken aboard, the herring 'took charge' and the remainder of the catch was lost. He hadn't seen the top bag with the mass of herring that was in the net and regretted not having had three boats round the net from the start. 'A've thought aboot that so many times,' he admitted ruefully. 'We dinna do it very well.' The Fairway became 'alive with herring' after that, and boats were shooting everywhere but 'cou'na take a scale off them when they wir disturbed'. [Archibald Paterson]

An 'up-an-dooner' at Corodale

Andy McCrindle, in common with most seasoned practitioners in the North, recalled many big rings there. One night he experienced an 'up-an-dooner' – a netful of herring that was proving difficult to raise – against the cliff-face on the south side of Corodale Bay, and the *May Queen* and *Seafarer* were called alongside to assist. His *Silver Fern* and the *Seafarer* were filled from that net and then the *May Queen* shot away up in the head of the bay. She and Andy's neighbour-boat, the *Silver Lining*, were filled from that ring. 'Jeest wi two rings, jeest lik that – there wir plenty o herrin about then.'

He recalled another ring in Loch Eport in the middle of a day in 1958 or '59. Manson of Mallaig had shot to haul into the north side of the loch, while the Ayrshiremen shot towards the south side. There wasn't a lot of room in the loch and the two middle net-buoys 'wir knockin against each other, Manson's and wir own'. Manson got nothing that time, but the three Ayrshire boats – *May Queen*, *Seafarer* and *Silver Fern* – were filled. The *Silver Fern* went aground twice that day – she 'rumped up on a shoal', but was undamaged because Ronnie Johnson was wiring for herring at the time and the boat was only moving at 'feeling speed'; then, at the mouth of the loch, her keel jammed in a cleft of rock and she had to be towed off, an accident which tore a big skelf of wood out of her, as was discovered much later. That same day, the *Silver Fern* chased a spot of herring up a 'sheugh', or creek, and followed the fish so far up that Andy hadn't room to turn the boat and was forced to back out. [Andy McCrindle]

Losing Herring
· · · · · · · · · · · · · · · · · · · ·

Fishermen hated to lose a catch of herring, having netted it in the first place, but there were occasions when, regardless of expertise, the herring 'took charge', as fishermen said, and plummeted en masse to the bottom or else burst the net by their sheer bulk. At other times, strong tide or the breakage of some vital piece of equipment led to the abandonment of a netful of herring. Not a few skippers pondered, for years afterwards, on how they might have saved a catch that eluded them by some mishap.

Seal Bay

The Jacksons went down to Seal Bay one night. It was blowing hard, south-west wind. They got a 'wee lee' in a corner along the land, saw herring on the echo-meter, let go the winky and canted off to shoot. On account of the bulk of herring, Neil Jackson told his crew not to blink the searchlight from the foredeck, which was normal practice. 'Damn me,' he recalled, 'did they no start blinkin the light!' And the neighbour-boat started blinking his light at the other end of the net. When the hauling of the net commenced, the crews were roaring that they couldn't hold on to her; the winch men kept heaving away on the sole until finally the rope was hauled right off the bottom guard of the net with the weight of herring 'blown oot'. The net was loaded, and once the rope came off, the herring went to the ground. It was a sandy bottom, and when the crews got the empty net back aboard, with the slime of the herring and the sand sticking to it, it was about the height of the wheelhouse roof, or twice its normal bulk.

They went into North Bay, sorted the net and put the sole-rope back on. In the afternoon, once the crew had finished the work and eaten dinner, Neil said to them: 'Right, boys, on yer gear; we'll go oot an we'll shot this net an we'll wash it.' They steamed off to the Curachan Bank, into deep water – 30, 40 fathoms – in broad daylight in the wintertime. A gannet came and struck and they shot round it. As they were hauling in the net, Neil noticed that the buoys were 'awfu heavy', but that was attributed to the weight of sand still on the net. But, no: 'The sole wis up an comin. There's a herrin mashed. We got a hunder-an-eighty cran.' [Neil Jackson]

Vatersay Sound

One winter, in the mid- to late-1960s, the *Storm Drift III* was 'working four boats' with the *Prospector, Valhalla* and *Girl Margaret*. The *Storm Drift's* crew shot on a big spot of herring in Vatersay Sound. It was a flat calm night and they'd just started to heave the net when 'all of a sudden this sea rose in the back o the net.' The crews thought it 'something exceptional'. It just rose and disappeared, and with it disappeared the net. This had been the herring rising in a mass at the back of the net and 'just flattenin right into the sand'. The crews were fully an hour recovering the net, which they could hardly haul for the sand that was on it. It was undamaged, but empty. The herring had flattened it on to the bottom in 10 fathoms of water. [Iain Gemmell]

The head of Loch Eynort

One one occasion, in the early 1950s, the Gemmells' *Summer Rose* and *Storm Drift* went alongside the *May Queen* and *Seafarer* to assist their crews with a netful of herring. After much 'struggle and strife', wrestling for hours with the net, the combined crews got the herring under control, but just as they were about to begin brailing, 'a strap broke, a mast went an we lost the lot'. [Iain Gemmell]

Loch Carnan

Matt Sloan in the *Watchful* was up in Loch Carnan one day, in the winter of 1968, along with the *Ocean Gem* and the *Saffron*. They had a big ring – the net was just floating up with herring – and the *Ocean Gem* came round and her crew caught the corks and tied up to the bag. Her crew started brailing before the *Watchful*'s men even went near the sling to get the herring dried in. Suddenly, as Matt recalled, 'everything went down'. He didn't know what started the herrings' plummet – perhaps it was the *Ocean Gem*'s commencement of brailing – but the herring burst the net before even 15 cran had been taken out of it. The three boats required a quota each – their respective neighbours had already gone to market – and they got them from the *Britannia* and the *Fair Morn* or *New Dawn*, who had rung further up the Fords and had plenty of herring left in the net. There were eight boats working in partnership at that time, the *Britannia, Fair Morn, New Dawn, Fair Wind, Storm Drift, Jasmine, Girl Margaret* and *Valhalla*. [Matt Sloan]

Loch Boisdale

Angus McCrindle recalling his brother Willie 'Pin' McCrindle in the *Saffron* ringing between the buoy and the shore in Loch Boisdale: 'We didnae get a chance at aa. Fae he lifted the gable en aboard, the herrin wis filterin oot through the wide[-meshed] wings, an we browsed on that for a month. What could we have done tae save these herrin? Nothing, really. The net wis jeest absolutely fou o herrin – that's what she wis. We never got a basket oot it. She burst. The mair they pu'ed the net in, the mair ye saw the herrin. Och, A don'know what wis in her – a thoosand cran or somethin.' [Angus McCrindle]

Diving Herring

'One afternoon we went into Vatersay Bay. The four boats – *Kittiwake*, *Kestrel*, *King Bird* and *King Fisher* – were together. Almost immediately we were in among herring, so thick they were, as we would say, "knocking lumps oot o the wire". One of the boats – I forget which – shot away. Everything went fine; a big shot dried up; neighbour-boat squared round, and the net strapped up. As soon as the brailer was dipped into the net, the herring took a dive, and no matter what we did, we couldn't get them up. We wrestled away for long enough, but eventually they took charge. We had to cut away and just stand back and let them go. We tried another ring, and although it was a smaller shot the result was the same.' [Neil Short, letter]

'Herring behaved in different ways when caught – sometimes they just went for the bottom, and you couldn't stop them. At other times, they were very easily handled, just blowing up by themselves. We got a ring, which I captured on 8mm cine, with nearly 600 cran just off Eriskay harbour one January day, and they were a doddle to handle. Another time we shot on the north side of Skiport, and we never saw them. They just went to the bottom, and we couldn't move them. There was a big ring in her, but we tried everything, including pouring coarse salt into the net. We ended up taking the lower bag away from the sling, and there wasn't a herring got near that spot for a long time. I think maybe they just suffocated and lay in a dead heap on the bottom.' [Tommy Ralston, letter]

Liberating herring

It was a habit of the Jacksons to release herring if the net contained much more than their own pair of boats could take, which might be 350 cran with the earlier boats and 400-plus with the later. 'A winna dream o shoutin another boat alongside,' Neil Jackson declared. The neighbour-boat would be taken round and once the bag of the net had been strapped to the boats' sides, it would be split and the herring in one half liberated. His reasoning was that by the time the Jacksons' own boats were filled, the remaining herring would be dead and their weight would burst the cotton net. 'An it used tae annoy some folk,' he admitted, 'but it wis my crew that wis mendin the net an it wis puttin me oot o action for the next night if A had a burst net that wisna mended.' [Neil Jackson]

Lost nets

Nets as well as herring were lost. Tide running between islands was sometimes so fierce that it would carry off whole nets, which might be recovered or might disappear altogether. On occasion, with a netful of herring to haul, a crew would be 'hangin on an hangin on' and making nothing of the task. 'As the herrin got deader, they got weightier.' A weak bit in the net might then give. Some crews kept a spare net ashore, but on the bigger boats the spare net was often stowed out of the way, on the starboard side. Latterly, after nylon nets were introduced, the danger of a burst was minimal, and a crew could 'tie up the bag o thir net wi the herrin in it' and wait until the neighbour had returned from market before dealing with the catch. [Duncan McSporran]

Angus Martin in the *Endeavour* shot out off Barra Head one day. The echo-meter showed a very black mark and Angus stretched the net well. When the crews began to boat the net, 'she went down oot o sight, floats an everything, an then she bounced up. We got the ropes, cork-rope an the sole-rope. The whole net wis gone. A good net – they jeest ran away wi the net.' [Angus Martin]

Markets and Money
●●●●●●●●●●●●●●●●●●●●●●

The main market-ports in the North were Gairloch, Mallaig and Oban, and which of these the herring were landed at depended on several factors, chief of which were. 1. Fishing grounds – which market offered the shortest run? 2. Weather conditions – which market offered the easiest crossing, taking into account wind force and direction? 3. Market conditions – where might the best prices be obtained?

The necessity of having to run catches across the Minch to market was probably the greatest handicap of the North fishing. Catching the herring was, in itself, generally a comfortable enough business, since most of the fishing was done inshore, where sheltered corners could be found in most conditions. The difficulties often arose when the time came to get catches across the Minch, as will be seen in the next chapter.

Crossing to market might only be the start of the problem. There was the return passage to make, and, if the weather deteriorated, the carrier-boat might end up storm-bound for days on end and unable to rejoin her neighbour-boat to resume fishing. For that reason, pairs of boats were frequently merged into combinations of four and six and even eight, so that, while some of the boats were away at market, the others could continue fishing.

The same reasoning led many ring-net skippers, particularly between the Wars, to engage the services of steam-drifters to run catches across the Minch in winter, allowing the ringers to continue the fishing operation uninterrupted. One half of the catches' market value went to the ring-net boats and the other half to the carrier, but the arrangement was none the less considered satisfactory. Clyde-based herring-buyers at times followed the ring-net fleets north, in the 'herring-steamers' they operated, and purchased catches on the fishing grounds. The large Dutch and German trawlers, known as 'Klondykers', also bought herring on the fishing grounds, and that market too was a boon in that it obviated a long haul to the mainland ports.

The universal measure in the herring fishery was the 'cran', introduced in 1815 and amounting to 37.5 gallons (170.48 litres) or roughly from 800 to 1000 herring, depending on their size. In the North, Clyde fishermen always reckoned their catches in crans, but when fishing home waters the term was never used. The working measure there was the 'basket', in which catches were discharged and which contained a quarter-of-a-cran.

Boxing herring

Catches of herring were ordinarily discharged from the net and stowed loose in the hold, but between the Wars the boxing of herring during the summer fishings became standard practice.

'Herring were boxed to keep them firm. If they lay in bulk in the hold, they, because of the feeding in them, became very soft and the result was many torn bellies. Buyers wouldn't accept herring in that condition. The boxes held something more than seven stone but it was accepted that four boxes made a cran. The main market in those days was the kippering market and herring had to be in very good condition.' [Neil Short, letter]

The practice of boxing of herring ended about 1958. The crews of the *Storm Drift* and *Summer Rose* lay at the back of Canna one night, selecting and boxing herring, and, when they sold the catch at Mallaig, received a better price for the 'bulk herring' than for the boxed. The boxes were put ashore that day and 'were never back abaird'. The boats, Iain Gemmell said, were not equipped for carrying boxes. About 100 empties were as many as they could take, and these 'slid aw ower the place' and left the fishermen with little space to work. [Iain Gemmell]

No brailing allowed

During the Minch summer fishings in the 1930s, buyers required ring-net fishermen to discharge herring from the net using the traditional basket instead of the far more efficient winch-operated brailer, the reasons being that, during the brailing operation, the compressed herring had the feeding squeezed out of them and their scales removed. This again was a boxing market. 'They're far nicer herrin taken aboard wi the basket,' Grieve Gemmell conceded. [Grieve Gemmell]

First pool best

Markets depended on the fishing and on the weather. If there were a lot of herring going, then prices would go down, but if you got a shot of herring on a breezy night and there wasn't a lot of herring going in, you would get a better price. Surplus herring was sold for fish-meal and 'chappie' – or petfood. Crews tried to reach market in time for the first 'pool', or sale, in the morning, but that obviously depended on when the herring had been caught. 'If ye got a good shot o herrin,' Joe Brown remarked, 'ye wir away lik hell for Mallaig tae try an get in the first pool … The prices went doon when ye wirna in wi early shots.' He experienced lying at Oban for two days waiting for a lorry to come and take the catch. [Joe Brown]

Decisions

The Sloans left Oban one Sunday just after midnight in the *Bairn's Pride* and the first *Wistaria* and arrived in Loch Skiport some time in the morning and dropped anchor. Late in the afternoon, they started searching there for herring. Billy shot and tore his net badly. Matt, his neighbour in the *Bairn's Pride*, went up into MacCormick's Bight and had a shot which yielded about 200 crans. The weather was poor, so the two boats went into the Kettle with the herring they had caught and dropped anchor there. At some time during that night, they got a weather forecast. About 6 o'clock that morning they got under way and left Loch Skiport, but they quickly realised that it wasn't a morning for attempting Mallaig, for the wind was pretty much southerly and blowing a strong gale. The two boats got up past Vaternish, and as they crossed Loch

Snizort the wind was 'absolutely smokin' coming off the Skye shore. They got up and round Ru Hunish and, passing Staffin Bay on the run south, happened to notice the masts of a trawler inshore. Such was the magnitude of the seas, they couldn't see the actual trawler – only the tops of her masts. She was lying at anchor there, so both boats dropped anchor alongside her.

This was now Tuesday, but they decided that, in the prevailing conditions, Gairloch was now out of the question. At about 10' clock at night, the wind eased and the moon appeared, lovely in a clear sky. They set off once again, Matt remarking to Billy as they got under way: 'Don't you think we're wastin oor time goin tae Gairloch? A really think we should gie a lot o thought tae goin tae Mallaig noo.' At that stage, Mallaig seemed the better choice to Matt, because they were now into Wednesday and at Gairloch, he reasoned, the best they could expect for the catch was fish-meal. 'Let's go tae Mallaig,' he insisted, 'an we can at least have a hope o gettin pet-food for these herrin.' – 'Aw,' Billy replied, 'tae blazes wi that. We've had them aboard long enough. Let's go tae Gairloch an get rid o them.' They arrived, later that morning, in Gairloch, and at sale time the first bid the auctioneer got for the herring was £8 a cran. 'We finished up we got nine poun a cran for these herrin, an these wir caught on Monday an landed in Gairloch on Wednesday. I think that is quite remarkable. An I thought I wis the one that wis gonny play safe by goin tae Mallaig tae get fifty shillins a cran as opposed tae fish-meal.' [Matt Sloan]

A fortune

The *Storm Drift II* and the *Summer Rose* had been at the north end of 'the beat' – the North Fords, Petersport, Uskavaig – on the Friday night. With nothing doing in the early hours of Saturday morning, a decision had to be taken on where to spend the week-end. Mallaig was too far, so the alternatives were 'tie tae a tree' or go to Loch Maddy. The two boats went to Loch Maddy. On Monday, the wind freshened. When the MacBrayne's steamer arrived, the boats left the quay and went out for a look. It wasn't weather for fishing, so when the steamer left, the two boats returned to the quay and didn't leave there all week except to allow the steamer to berth on the Wednesday and again on the Friday. By the following Monday, there had evidently been no boats at sea anywhere in Scotland for seven days. When the steamer arrived on that Monday, the boats went out to lie at anchor in a bay on the south side of Loch Maddy.

There are at least two versions of what happened in that bay. One was that one of the young cooks, whose bed in the forecastle was below the boat's waterline, heard herring playing through the hull. The other, more credible version is that Sammy Gemmell on the *Storm Drift* was 'doin his usual thing, up when the rest of us wir sleepin, watching what was goin on'. He had gone on deck and noticed that the wind had fallen away; then he heard herring playing all round the boat. The crews were roused, the net shot, and 140 cran of herring secured. The catch was taken to Gairloch, where it sold at £7 a cran, a 'fortune' in the early 1950s. That isolated landing and its impact on a starved market made the national news and 'Sam and John Gemmell were mentioned in despatches'. The crews had 'a party' in Gairloch, took the boats to Oban and caught a train home from there. [Iain Gemmell]

Huge herring

The *Lily* and her neighbour, the *Fionnaghal* of Tarbert, had a 'wile bad run' in the Skye lochs in the summer of 1942 and decided to head home. On passage, they saw another pair – the *Jessie* of Tarbert (Archie Kerr) and *Enterprise* of Campbeltown (Willie MacDonald) – going down through the Sound of Canna and they decided to investigate. It transpired that the other pair had got nothing at all and were 'away hame wi hunger'; but, having seen a gannet 'lookin great' off the Jyle Rock, the new arrivals decided to remain. A shot was secured that night, on a 'blue flash' in the phosphorescence, and 75 cran taken aboard. The herring were huge, measuring from the tips of Davie's fingers to the bend of his arm. It was remarked in Mallaig that these were the biggest herring landed there for more than 20 years, the last such having come from Tiree Bank. Had it not been for wartime control, the catch would have fetched a much higher price. [David McNaughton]

At a Klondyker

Iain Gemmell's first experience of landing to a Klondyker – or 'lugger' as fishermen called them – was in Loch Nevis, north of Mallaig. The crew was directed to a German vessel and went alongside to discharge. He remembered about 20 young fellows seated in a circle with two baskets between their legs, gutting herring. The herring were being supplied to them by another fellow with a bag-net on a pole, which he was dipping into the pound where the Ayrshire crew was unloading its catch and constantly swinging round to the baskets at the boys' feet.

Every now and again, he would stick a bottle of beer in the gutters' mouths and give them a drink. 'They wir like prisoners,' Iain Gemmell recalled. 'By the time we left, they had still a lot tae do, an there wis another boat waitin tae start, so it looked as if they wir goin tae be there for a long time.' [Iain Gemmell]

Money

Some Campbeltown crews in the North customarily sent money home – £5 or £10 weekly, depending on the success of the fishing – but as a rule Ayrshire and Tarbert crews didn't. When the trip was over and the crews back home, expenses would be deducted and the remaining money shared between the boats themselves and the crew-members. The general division was a share to each crew-member and three to each boat, though boys usually started on a half-share and graduated to a full share.

Robert Ross recalled a trip across from Loch Eynort in a blizzard around 1950 when the McDougall crews were returning home for New Year. When they reached Crinan to board the bus for Tarbert, the *Mairearad*'s skipper, Donald McDougall, remarked: 'Well, I gave a sigh o relief when we got the Soon o Mull.' – 'How's that, Donal?' somebody queried. 'A'd three thousand two hunder poun below ma pillow,' was the reply. One notable Tarbert skipper was supposed to have kept his money in a barrel under the bed, his reasoning being that, 'It wid be easy enough tae rowl it oot if the hoose went on fire!'

In the North, Iain Gemmell recalled, the Ayrshire fishermen 'existed on subs', which they obtained from the skipper each week-end. The expenses and wages were squared up at the end of the trip. In later years, however, the fish-salesmen in the relevant ports sent earnings and expenses to the boats' accountants at home and cheques – weekly – to the crew members' families. The final balance was made at the end of the trip.

There was, in the early years anyway, a degree of flexibility in the division of money. Grieve Gemmell has known his father take nothing for the boat's shares if the fishing was slack. 'The boat doesnae eat,' Sammy reasoned. Fishermen certainly suffered financial slacks, when herring were scarce or prices were low or turbulent weather kept them in harbour, but herring fishermen forever lived with the hope of a magnificent redeemer, or 'touch', that would wipe out debts and fill their pockets with money. And that did happen, and happen repeatedly to the most successful of crews.

Grieve Gemmell recounted, albeit diffidently, one week when he and his neighbour had 'the fou o the boats' in Mallaig every day and were the only boats in. It was a three-week trip and the money would be divided at the end of the trip, but had that week's earnings been divided there and then, each man on the boat would have received £1120 or £1130 in wages, which was big money in 1967. The bulk of that money came from a couple of big rings in Shepherd's Bay, which filled the five boats – *Storm Drift*, *Valhalla*, *Girl Margaret*, *Prospector* and *Britannia* – that were working in company.

There is, of course, another side of the story to tell, albeit with just one example here. Shortly after George Newlands of Campbeltown got married in 1931, he was 10 weeks fishing in the North and earned only £2 for the whole period.

Crossing the Minch

Of all the subjects covered in this book, this one seldom failed to stimulate at least one outstanding memory, for Minch crossings in winter were often dramatic and occasionally life-threatening. The analogy with submarines was not infrequently used, and Andy McCrindle of Maidens recalled Tarbertman Ronnie Johnson telling him that, during one crossing in the Mairearad, *'they surfaced twice before they got tae Mallaig'! For the most conscientious of skippers, however, the anxiety was not confined to the actual crossing to market; it extended to the return crossing and the possibility of being storm-bound in the market port or on passage across, as a consequence of which valuable fishing time would be lost.*

The first Clyde boats to work ring-nets in the North were Loch Fyne skiffs. These craft were built for sail, and, in their pure form, never exceeded 40ft (12.19m) in length. Their herring-carrying capacity (generally fewer than 75 crans) was small and their capabilities for running catches across the Minch were – certainly in winter – limited.

It was the post-1922 generation of decked and canoe-sterned ring-netters, bred from Robert Robertson's innovative Falcon *and* Frigate Bird *of Campbeltown, that exploited the potential of the Minch herring fisheries to the full. They were shallow-draughted and highly manoeuvrable, undoubted advantages when working tight to the shore, and it was said of them that they could 'float on the dew' and 'turn on a sixpence'.*

The ringers were lovely, built with flowing lines for speed and ease of handling. Their names, too – recurring throughout this book – were lovely. The

Ayrshiremen, in particular, had a talent for choosing or constructing poetic iden-tities for their craft, as: Storm Drift, Fair Wind, Fair Morn, Golden West, Arctic Moon, Valhalla, Night Hawk, Pathfinder, Southern Sun, Ocean Gem, New Dawn, Jasmine, Wistaria, Watchful, Sapphire, Saffron, Summer Rose, Dewy Rose.

Amazed

There were times when the ring-net boats lay in Castlebay in gales of wind, getting out in the afternoon and having a ring. Those crews who were unsuccessful returned to Castlebay in the dark, while the successful crews went across the Minch. On one particular occasion, there was a fleet of Fleetwood trawlers stormbound there, waiting to proceed to the Iceland fishing grounds, and the trawlermen were 'amazed at the fishin that wis goin on round about them and by the size o the boats an the trips they wir makin'. [Iain Gemmell]

Impressed

'I was back in Boisdale on holiday in the early '70s and met the local postman who told me of how he and the other schoolboys were fasci-nated with the ringers and the way they could be manoeuvred in comparison with the older Eriskay boats, which were, in the main, heavily-built, under-powered Zulus.' [Neil Short, letter]

'The fast Clyde boats ...'

'My earliest recollection of the Clyde men round Eriskay was in my school days, maybe 1933 or '34. I remember names like *Falcon, Frigate Bird, Blue Bird, Kittiwake* and *Kestrel.* I was eight years of age then and used to keep a look-out for the fast Clyde boats with the sun glistening on their varnished hulls.' [Duncan MacInnes, letter]

'Good, able boats'

'They wir good, able boats. Better wi the wee drap o herrin in them ... sixty, seeventy cran wis jeest lovely. That wis them jeest nicely balanced an they winna move so much. But a load o herrin ... ye take a hunner an fifty cran on a boat, it's a big load. A mean, they're away doon tae the top bend. You're crossin the Minch wi the ould eighty-eight [88hp Kelvin engine] clickin away.' [Joe Brown]

Above The crew of the *Watchful*, 1969. L – R, Andy Alexander, Billy McCrindle, Skipper Matt Sloan, Hugh Alexander, Jimmy Gibson and John Watson. Matt's daughter Dierdre is in the wheelhouse. Per Matt Sloan, Maidens.

Below The four McDougall brothers of Tarbert and crews, c 1935. Back row, from left: George Arthur McFarlane, Archie McFarlane, Peter McDougall, Peter Johnson, Donald McDougall (skipper, *Fionnaghal*). Front row, from left: Robert McFarlane, Alex McDougall, Archie McDougall (skipper, *Mairearad*), Calum McFarlane. Per Peter McDougall, Tarbert.

Above The *Stella Maris* in the sea-lock at Crinan, her neighbour the *Fiona* ahead of her, as the fishermen prepare to leave their boats in the Canal and have a week-end at home, having been fishing at Canna in the summer of 1964. The two cooks, Norman Thomson and John Reid, are on the starboard side of the *Stella*; Jim Meenan is in the wheelhouse; from aft, going forward, Campbell MacBrayne, Davie Paterson, Joe Brown and Duncan Wilkinson, with Alec Brown (left) and Walter Brown on the starboard quarter of the *Fiona*. Photograph by Tom Weir.

Below Sammy Gemmell's *Storm Drift*, entering Dunure harbour at the end of a passage home from Mallaig on 10 June, 1939. She is a basic ring-netter, built solely for that job, and predates the advent of electronic navigational and fish-finding equipment. Her wheelhouse would have contained only a compass. Dan McDonald Collection.

Above Matt Sloan's *Watchful* of Maidens steaming north-west of the Heisgeir, on passage to Loch Boisdale, c 1966. The only outward signs of the electronic era, which the ring-net fleets had by then entered, are the wireless aerial and appurtenances. Photograph by Angus McCrindle.

Below Andy 'Tarry' McCrindle's *Aliped IX* of Girvan at North Bay, Barra, c 1972. She represents the final generation of well-equipped ring-netters, built, in fuller proportions, for both-ringing and trawling. Photograph by Phil McCabe, Peterhead.

Above Neil Jackson's *Village Belle III* of Tarbert, her forefoot clean out of the water as she clears Girvan harbour, 1967. Photograph by Geoff Webster, Fleetwood.

Below Battering through a head-sea in the North, Johnny McMillan's *Elma* of Carradale, c 1953. Per Alistair McMillan, Carradale.

Left Hauling a ring-net, Moonen Bay, Skye, c 1952. The crew on the *Stella Maris* of Campbeltown is: L-R, Duncan McIsaac, Skipper Jock Meenan, Cecil Finn, Jim Meenan and Denis Meenan. The haul yielded about 30 cran of herring. Per Denis Meenan, Campbeltown.

Below The *Watchful* and *Wistaria* of Maidens 'squared' in Corodale Bay, South Uist, with a catch of 130 crans of herring, 1960. The catch is being brailed on board the *Watchful*. Per Matt Sloan, Maidens.

Above The *Watchful* and *Saffron* of Maidens brailing herring in Loch Carnan on a January morning, c 1965. Photograph by Angus McCrindle.

Below The ring-net fleet on a bustling Mallaig morning, c. 1951. Empty herring baskets are being swung back into two of the discharging boats from the rail-trucks on the quay and the stove in the foreground boat is reeking well. The *Elizabeth Campbell* of Carradale (CN 186) lies broadside in the middle of the picture, her crew assembled at the wheelhouse. McDougall Negatives, Carradale. Per L Paterson.

Above Duncan Ritchie (L) and George McMillan returning to the *Mairi Bhan* of Carradale with loaves of bread purchased at the shop in North Bay, Barra, 1951. McDougall Negatives, Carradale. Per L Paterson.

Below Breakfast of fried bacon and eggs and baked beans in the forecastle of the *Kittiwake* of Campbeltown, about 1950. The forward top bunks can be seen dimly at the top of the picture. L – R: skipper-owner John Wareham, Willie Scally and Archibald 'Scone' Black. From the late Lachie McDougall, Campbeltown. The Author's collection.

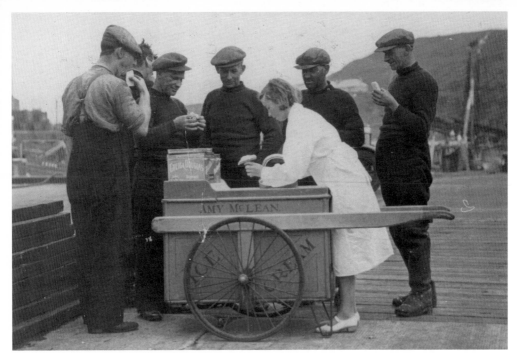

Above Enjoying Amy McLean's ice-cream at Mallaig on a Saturday morning, c 1935, L-R Jock McIntyre and Sandy McKinlay (the *King Fisher*), Archie Stewart and Malcolm McLean (the *King Bird*), John Short Sr (the *Nulli Secundus*) and Charlie Durnin (the *Bluebird*). Per Neil Short, Glasgow.

Below Archibald 'Baldy' Stewart at Buckingham Palace, receiving the British Empire Medal he was awarded for the service he performed when a Sunderland aircraft crashed in Loch Boisdale on 4 May, 1942. With him are his wife, May, and daughters Mary (L) and Ria. Per Mrs Doreen Wareham, Campbeltown.

A black mark

In the matter of Minch crossings in bad weather, Matt Sloan conceded that, on reflection, many fishermen would think themselves 'remarkably lucky on occasions'. In crossing loaded to the mainland from the Hebrides, however, the 'redeemin feature' was that, with the prevailing south-westerly to westerly winds, the passage was usually comparatively easy because the wind would mainly be on the boat's quarter or stern. The question, for most skippers, he said, was not, 'Are we gonny get tae market?', but, 'Is the weather gonny be suitable tae allow us tae get back?' The island of Canna was always the 'half-way house', but the majority of skippers hesitated to go into Canna, because, if they did so, that night's fishing could be discounted. 'If ye got up in the mornin,' he said, 'an discovered … ye heard somebody on the air; they're goin for Mallaig or Oban wi herrin aboard, ye think there's a black mark against ye for goin intae Canna. True!' [Matt Sloan]

Preparations

The best of the crews had an unvarying routine to perform before crossing. First, the catch would be consolidated in the hold with baskets and boards jammed in; then the tarpaulin would be secured over the hold – some crews weighting it with anchor chain for good measure – and, finally, the net would be lashed down on the stern. 'An they jeest went away an forgot aboot it because if ye shut the throttle a wee bit they wid go forever.' [Iain Gemmell]

First boat into Mallaig

The *Endeavour* left the mouth of Loch Boisdale for Mallaig one dark night with 96 cran of herring aboard. Twelve other boats left with her to cross the Minch, and she was the only boat that reached Mallaig that night. Some of them sought shelter in the Skye lochs 'upside o Canna', while others ran for Rum. The *Endeavour* was going across in company with several 'BA men' – Ayrshiremen, from their port of registration, Ballantrae – and they shouted her skipper, Angus Martin, on the radio, and advised him to follow them into a 'wee harbour' in Rum. 'A never wis in it,' he told them, 'an A'm afraid tae go in't.' So he battered on through the gale and reached Mallaig at 4 a.m. The *Endeavour*'s catch fetched £10 a cran in the market, and some of the buyers asked Angus were there any other boats coming. 'Aye,' he said, 'they'll maybe be in later on.' The next boat arrived at 9 a.m. She was the *May* of Girvan, skippered by James McCreath, and her catch sold at £10 10s. The remainder of these dozen boats that set out with the *Endeavour* didn't appear until Saturday evening and Sunday morning, and their catches were sold at a low price, for fish-meal. Andrew 'Bomber' Brown in the *Mairi Elspeth* somehow ended up in Loch Bracadale and lay there for three days with 100 cran of herring, which he finally had to dump. Angus Martin's son, Alistair, was one of the crew that night, and when the *Endeavour* returned home after that trip North, Alistair left and went back to his trade as a joiner. 'Never again!' he vowed. [Angus Martin]

A reprimand

Robert Ross recalled crossing to Mallaig from the West Side in the *Mairearad* one night. The Jacksons had earlier run across with about 50 cran in each boat, but the *Mairearad* had about 150 cran aboard and was absolutely awash as she made the crossing. Having berthed in Mallaig, Robert Ross was despatched to the market with a sample of the catch. He met Willie Jackson Sr on the quay, and the older man quizzed him: 'Did ye get a puckle?' – 'Aye,' Robert replied, 'a hunder, a hunder an odd cran, Willie.' All Willie said in reply was: 'Ye've a fuckin cheek comin across on a day lik this.' His implication was that the boat had been dangerously overloaded for the conditions.

Donald and Peter McDougall in the neighbour-boat 'wore a track in Boisdale Quay' until Archie McDougall telephoned to say that the *Mairearad* had reached Mallaig. There was no radio in the *Mairearad* at that time, and it was that experience decided the McDougalls to have one installed. 'It's great the way there wir no boats lost,' Robert Ross mused. 'Mind, they wir clever boats. It wis a way o life then. God, if ye took the [present-day fishermen] away for a month now, they wid be cuttin thir thrott efter three or four days. They've got tae get ashore for a shave an a shower.' [Robert Ross]

Loaded to the hatches

The first time the Jacksons filled the *Village Belle III* – capacity, 225 cran – 'she wis some sight comin oot o Eriskay, her lodded tae the gunnels, lodded tae the bloody hatches'. During the passage across, one of the crewmen, Archie 'Rigger' McKinnon, came into the wheelhouse to relieve the skipper, Neil Jackson. 'Away ye go below – A'll take her noo,' he said. 'Well,' Neil cautioned, 'jeest bloody waatch her, Erchie. A know she's a big boat, but she's got a big cargo as well.' She was 'goin tae the hilt' at the time, and, as Neil reasoned, although the boat was bigger than any of the earlier Jackson ringers, she was also carrying a bigger cargo and was consequently heavier. 'Christ,' Neil recalled, 'afore A got below, he damnt near waashed me over the side!' [Neil Jackson]

Pleading

When Neil Jackson first went to the North with his father, it was different. The old men never loaded the boats to cross the Minch. He saw his father, with 100 cran in the net, put 50 cran into each boat, satisfied with that. On occasion, Neil had to plead with him to shoot again. One night, there were 100 cran aboard and his father decided: 'That'll do.' But it was a fine night for crossing and Neil protested. 'Good God, there's no herrin in it anywhere. We'd better get another shot.' Having got his father to agree, 'we went away an we shot. We come fast an tore the net. We got fifteen cran oot her. An then A'm damned but he shot himsel an he got another hundred cran, an that wis it – offski!' [Neil Jackson]

'When you learn tae fish them ...'

The crew that made the run to market had the Minch crossing to undertake, often in nasty weather, the catch to sell and discharge, and, finally, the run back across to the fishing ground to rejoin the neighbour-boat. There were no hard and fast rules governing the running of herring. Latterly, the arrangement was generally turn about, but the earlier practice among most crews was, as Robert Ross put it: 'If you caught them, yer neebor ran them.' This, however, sometimes led to devious work, when one skipper would purposely shoot on very little herring – perhaps 15 or 20 cran – which committed his neighbour to running not only that catch, but all subsequent catches, unless, of course, both boats ended up loaded, in which case both would make the trip. In the story below, the crew of the Oaklea *had become demoralised with its repeated task of running herring.*

One night on the Curachan Bank, Willie Jackson Sr shot, and the catch was put aboard the *Oaklea*, a Jackson boat, but skippered by Dougie Smith. 'Right,' said Willie, 'off ye's go.' All his crew on the *Village Belle II* was laughing. His young son, Neil, was crewing on the *Oaklea* and protested: 'Christ, are ye naw goin tae take herrin aboard that boat at all? Are you no thinkin o takin a run at all, instead o us runnin back an furrid, back an furrid?' His father replied: 'Ma boy, when you learn tae fish them, A'll run them.' [Neil Jackson]

A tied throttle

A fleet of boats left Mallaig one day in a westerly gale, among them the *Manx Rose*, an Isle of Man ringer, skippered by an East Coastman (evidently one Lachie Horsburgh) who had married and settled in Peel, and crewed by Campbeltown men. A mile or so west of Sleat Point, on Skye, the skipper tried to ease down the boat to meet a rising sea, but couldn't – the engineer had tied the throttle! She rose on the sea and crashed down violently, and Willie McKenzie put his head up the forecastle hatch and shouted to the skipper to come and see what he had done. Henry Martin was at the back of the wheelhouse and, when the skipper emerged, he asked Henry to take the wheel. When the skipper came up out of the forecastle, he shouted to Henry to keep her before the sea and go back to Mallaig. There was an East Coast boat abreast of the *Manx Rose* and she too canted and returned to Mallaig.

One of her crew came over in Mallaig and remarked that many's the time he'd heard it said, 'she wis airborne,' but hadn't believed it until then – the whole boat, keel and all, had lunged out of the water! The heavy water-tank in the *Manx Rose* had tumbled into the boat's bottom, carrying everything before it, and the stove was wrecked. [Henry Martin]

Into Tobermory

The *Fiona* left Loch Boisdale one Friday morning along with four other boats. The *Stella Maris* had 90 cran aboard and the others had nothing. Denis Meenan and Wattie Brown were sitting in the wheelhouse in a south-easterly gale, the boat 'bouncin an bangin', and could see the stern-lights of the other boats disappearing ahead. While the two of them sat all night in the cramped wheelhouse, the rest of the crew were turned in. 'They must've been sleepin,' Denis recalled, 'but how they slept A don'know!' Finally, Denis decided: 'That'll dae, Wattie. We're gan intae Tobermory here an we're gonny haev wir breakfast, an the rest o them can come up.' Battering through solid water, they took nine hours getting into Tobermory. [Denis Meenan]

Anchor overboard

One night, running for Ardnamurchan in a southerly gale, Cecil Finn and Campbell MacBrayne – boots and oilskins still on – were in their beds on the *Stella Maris*: 'It wis the best place to be – ye had naewhere else tae go anyway.' They were hearing the repeated bang of the anchor-stock striking the boat's rail above them, and Campbell said to Cecil: 'We should've tightened up that strop on the anchor, afore we wir absolutely under wey.' The hitch had slipped a bit, leaving six or seven inches of 'play' in the lashing. 'Well,' Cecil replied, 'it'll haev tae be that way noo anyway – that's for sure.' After a time, the banging stopped completely, and Campbell remarked: 'A think … A've the uncanny feelin that anchor's away. Ye know, A think it is, Cecil. A think we'd better get up.' When they got up on deck, they discovered that the hitches on the bitts had altogether loosened off and that the anchor, 15 fathoms of chain and 60 fathoms of cable had gone over the side; so they had to haul it all back aboard, in a gale of wind an hour from Ardnamurchan. 'Boys, it wis horrendous,' Cecil recalled, 'gettin that anchor tae the winch!' [Cecil Finn]

The *Undaunted*

On a night just before Christmas of 1958, the *Harvest Queen* left Castlebay to go home to Carradale. The brothers Archie and Dougie Paterson were very methodical aboard the boat and had courses and times calculated, but this night there was a gale of south-east wind and it was nearly impossible to see anything with the boat battering into a head-sea and showering spray. They were steering a course for the Sound of Mull and were due to pass the notorious rocks called the Cairns of Coll, but there was no sign of the low beacon on the Cairns; they steamed another while, but still no sign. It was the only time Neil McDougall saw his skipper, Archie Paterson, flustered and anxious. Archie gave a shout on his radio and got an answer from the skipper of a big Leith-registered seiner. 'Give me a good long shout on the wireless an A'll put the DF on ye,' the 'Eastie' instructed. The Carradale men had no idea what this 'DF' was, but Archie complied and shortly afterwards the Eastie came back with the information: 'Another quarter an oor an ye'll see the Cairns light.' With the wind dead on the *Harvest Queen*'s stem, she hadn't been making the time she normally would have made. The DF, Neil McDougall later discovered, was a direction-finder. 'A wis never more pleased tae hear anybody comin back,' Neil recalled, 'an A'll always remember the boat's name – the *Undaunted*.' [Neil McDougall]

'All hands intae the wheelhoose'

One night the *Stella Maris* and *Regina Maris* were crossing with the *Golden Fleece* for Mallaig in south-west wind. There was a 'hell of a sea' running and a drifter was lost that night crossing the Minch; still, the 'cook' George McIntyre, Joe Brown and – perhaps – Campbell MacBrayne were turned in down below and getting some sleep, feeling the motion of the boat, but not hearing the shriek of the wind. Jock, Jim, and Denis Meenan were in the wheelhouse with Cecil Finn, who, as the gale worsened, was sent below to rouse the sleeping men. He gave them a shake and told them: 'Ye'd better come up tae the wheelhouse – all hands intae the wheelhoose!' Joe Brown recalled that night as one of the worst that he ever experienced crossing the Minch. The waving masthead light of the little *Golden Fleece* could be glimpsed up ahead only now and again as it cleared the tops of the intervening seas. They were glad to get into Mallaig, but water had got among the herring and the catch was floating in the hold, a mess. [Joe Brown]

A sudden storm

One Friday night the *Bairn's Pride* and *Wistaria* lay for several hours in Loch Boisdale. Billy Sloan in the *Wistaria* had a badly-torn net and the neighbouring crew decided to assist with the mending of it. It was a night of thick drizzle, and visibility was consequently poor. Around midnight, the mending was discontinued, because the *Wistaria* had herring – about 60 cran – to run to market. Billy decided to head for Gairloch, reckoning that he might gain on the price there. Just off Uisnish, while steaming for the north end of Skye, the wind suddenly – 'like a clap of thunder' – got up from the north-west.

It hit the *Wistaria* so violently that Billy Sloan decided it wasn't a night for going anywhere. One of the crewmen, Tom Harvey, later recalled that they heard the wind before it actually reached them; they knew there was wind coming. Billy dodged the *Wistaria* back in below Uisnish Light and the crew cleared the deck and tidied the net. The *Bairn's Pride* had gone into South Boisdale and dropped anchor, but before the crew could even turn in 'there wis this racket o wind, an it wis howlin'. They got the anchor up and got the *Bairn's Pride* out off that south side of the Loch and edged her north-north-east until the flashing buoy off Calvay Island opened up. The *Bairn's Pride* had an 88 hp 'Kelvin' engine in her at that time, and even with that power, Matt Sloan doubted that they would manage to reach the pier against the onslaught of the storm; but they did. Meantime, Matt was calling and calling the neighbour-boat on the radio, but couldn't make contact because, unknown to him, the *Wistaria*'s radio had been switched over to a light entertainment station. The only response Matt received was from an Eriskay ringer, the *Lady of Fatima*, at that time neighbouring the *Moira* of Campbeltown. The *Lady* had left Eriskay to run for Mallaig, but turned back when the storm broke. After several hours, the wind gradually moderated, and Billy Sloan felt more confident about crossing to market, but instead of running north for Gairloch, he instead chose Mallaig as the safer option, and that's where the *Wistaria* took the catch. [Matt Sloan]

The account below tells of the same night, but from the perspective of a crew-member of the Lady of Fatima, *the Eriskay ringer that attempted the Minch crossing and was forced back.*

'During our time with Matthew Speed of the *Moira* we enjoyed a good fishing. One winter we teamed up with the *Fiona* and *Acacia* – Matthew McDougall – just before we finished for the Christmas and New Year break, 1959. The *Acacia* went to Oban with a good shot; then two nights later the *Fiona* followed, also with a good shot; then home for the festive season.

'That left the *Moira* and ourselves. We were at the mouth of Barra Sound that evening. It was a Friday and when we passed the Calf, off the small island of Gighay, we saw the echo-sounder turning black from the keel to the bottom, which was 10 or 12 fathom. We steamed into the Sound, which should now be about 6 fathom where we were, but still black; so, to make sure it was not a fake picture on the Kelvin Hughes, we put out the feeling-wire and there was no doubt about it. The wire was vibrating with solid herring. We burst the net on this occasion. The *Moira*'s net was on shore, also in tatters. We went into North Bay and started lacing the big split, which we finally finished by 1 o'clock on Saturday morning, and back out to sea.

'We only went as far as Seal Bay at Gighay's east end. We rung and got 70 cran, enough for a night. I noticed it was a very inky black dark night but we steamed into Eriskay South Harbour. The barometer was rock-bottom. One had a feeling that all hell was in the air. After a cup of tea – this was about 4 AM and still black – I was told to start the 88 Kelvin. These were handle-start – no starter motor, no press button. I heard Angus [MacIsaac] saying to Norman [MacInnes, the skipper], "If I was you I would hug the shore till we see what's up with the glass", but Norman put her nose for the Minch.

'It was a near-fatal decision. We would be about three-quarters of an hour out when the hurricane hit us from the north-west, screaming winds and very high seas. Then, after a while, Norman put her about, for it was the only thing he could do. When he took her about, all the mattresses on the starboard side fell out; also the stove gave a lurch, but it held. Then we were in for a merciless pounding. Two of us were trapped in the forecastle. We did not know how things were in the wheel-house. Things were going OK till the net started going over the side. I don't right know what superhuman effort the four older hands put in, but they managed to secure it. Some one was looking after us. How long we kept hammering and pounding against it! It felt like hours. We tried to surface up the hatch, only there was no hatch.

'Then it was a while before the motion started easing down. We knew we were getting near land somewhere. It was now near 7.30 in the morning and still dark. The other Duncan MacInnes and I managed to scramble up to the bow, on our knees, and could make out land – it was the Calf at Barra Sound. We tagged down to Eriskay Harbour and along-side the *Moira*. Matt Speed said: 'Glad to see you back.'

'Anyway, it appears Billy Sloan was sheltering at Ushinish Light, also caught in the hurricane, but, unlike us, Billy was in shelter. The damage to our hull was the galvanised straps parted with the belting; we lost the navigation lights; the net leads, which were heavy; the scuttle on the hatch. Apart from a lot of water in the engine-room, we were OK. The engine was our saviour also. The man at the wheel, cool and calm. I would not have been writing this if he had not kept the head. Also, hats off to the man that built the *Lady of Fatima* – James Noble, Fraserburgh.

'I once asked Norman how did he cope that morning. He said that he took heart that Black John [MacInnes], the *St Columba*'s skipper, was there to encourage him, along with the rest of the crew. But he said, 'There was also a far greater power than me to guide us through'. Norman was a true Christian – far greater than us. We prayed as we never prayed since.

'That Saturday morning we left for Mallaig at 10 o'clock and got in at 2.30, a record passage, and the seas were tremendous, but no wind. Sloan was there and we got £15 a cran, well-earned. We were home at 12 o'clock that night.' [Duncan MacInnes, letter]

A long haul to Canna

One night, in the winter of 1956, the wee *Mairearad* left Uisinish Light with 90 cran of herring on board for Mallaig. In favourable conditions, the first stage of the crossing, to Canna, would have taken short of three hours, but that night it took eight-and-a-half hours, and the boat was pushed no further, for she'd been punching her way through moun-tainous seas in a south or south-easterly gale. She lay at Canna all that day and completed the crossing the day after, and despite the catch being 'over days', the price was good enough because there was little or no herring landed elsewhere. That was Peter McDougall's first year at the fishing and his first winter in the North; it was also the worst crossing that he ever experienced, and the closest he ever saw a boat come to being lost. 'That wis the nearest ever,' he recalled. 'Nobody ever spoke aboot it.' [Peter McDougall]

Damage west of Canna

The *Jasmine* came out of Mallaig one day, on passage back to the fishing grounds at Loch Boisdale. The skipper, Willie Anderson, had turned in, but his rest was thoroughly disrupted when, off the west end of Canna, the weight of water the boat was shipping hammered the seine-net winch down through the deck and cracked three beams. Damage notwithstanding, the *Jasmine* completed the trip across, had a successful night's fishing and returned to Mallaig loaded the next morning. That day, in the boatyard at Mallaig, iron shoes were made and fitted to the damaged beams, as a temporary repair. Willie took his boat back to Mallaig three days in succession, and had the beams replaced in the yard. [William Anderson]

'Those Magnificent Men in their Flying Machines'

One of the worst crossings experienced by Grieve Gemmell can be dated to the day that two Concordes – the Anglo-French supersonic passenger aircraft – took off simultaneously, one in Britain and the other in France. The *Storm Drift* was steaming out by Canna, and Grieve and David 'Inky' Edgar were in the wheelhouse listening to the live commentary on the radio. All of a sudden, the *Storm Drift* hit a lump of sea, lifted clean out of the water and came back down with a crash. The wireless set came off the wall, struck Grieve on the back of the head, and that was it silenced; but they picked up the set, got it back into the case and managed to reconnect the aerial wire using an aluminium ring-pull that was lying on the wheelhouse floor. When the reception returned, 'Those Magnificent Men in their Flying Machines' was playing – the Concordes were up and away! Beams had been broken, and the language of the first man out of the forecastle after the smash would have been unprintable had it been considered fit to repeat in the first place! [Grieve Gemmell]

A blizzard

The *Storm Drift III*'s first trip North, neighbouring the *Jasmine*, was a very eventful one. On one occasion she was crossing in company with the *Pathfinder* and *May Queen* for a week-end at home. They left Loch Boisdale at mid-day in a light southerly wind, but before they reached the Heisgeir they were in a gale of south-east wind and the boats were 'burying' themselves in the seas. Then a blizzard came on. The *Storm Drift* was the only boat in the fleet at that time with a Decca Navigator installed, but such was the weather that the aerial had 'spun up' and the navigator was rendered useless. The whole crew was in the wheelhouse, and Grieve Gemmell, the skipper, remarked that they should come to a lee in the wind if the course and time were right. A lull did come, and he gambled on their being in the lee of Ardnamurchan and accordingly drew a course from there to Rudha na Gall. The other three boats were 'talked in' and they too struck the lee. They 'picked up Rudha na Gall no bother', got into Tobermory and decided to go no further.

When the crew of the *Storm Drift* went below, they found that, with the boat's violent motions, the formica lining in the forecastle had split in several places at the screw-holes. The *Jasmine*'s stove was so badly broken that her crew flung it over the side. The *Pathfinder*'s skipper asked if the *Storm Drift*'s Decca aerial could be cleared so that the boats could carry on down the Sound of Mull for Oban, but the request was 'promptly refused'. When the boats left the next morning, the snow had ceased but there was still a gale of wind. Word was received on passage that the railway and road at Corpach was blocked with snow, so they went to the Crinan Canal and left the boats there, but discovered that the road between Lochgilphead and Glasgow was also blocked with snow. The lock-keeper at Crinan, however, suggested that they get a bus from Crinan to Tarbert and there catch the ferry which at that time ran to Greenock, and that's what they did. They returned to the boats the following – Sunday – night, and that was their week-end break over! [Iain Gemmell]

No smoke for 'Butcher'

'The *Acacia* and neighbour-boat, the *Mairi Bhan*, some seasons spent approximately six months of the year fishing in the infamous stormy waters we called the North. We'd be crossing and recrossing the Minches dozens and dozens of times, landing catches at Oban, Mallaig and Gairloch. I vividly remember one time, on passage from Mallaig to the

Outer Hebrides, the *Acacia* butting into a head-on gale, standing on deck, sheltering close in behind the wheelhouse, leaning against the mizzen mast for an eight-hour period. I was along with the other crew-member who had to stand in the lee of the wheelhouse, left out to face the elements, the wheelhouse being too small to accommodate all the crew. Out of a crew of six, only four could stand jammed upright in the wheel-house. Our waterproof working gear was a knee-length oilskin frock, or 'doper', and rubber thigh-boots. On this particular unforgettable passage, the seas just swept over the wheelhouse and came down off the roof on top of us. We indeed had the best of oilskins, and, by God, we needed them! In such severe weather, I always donned my genuine (lifeboat style) sou'wester. It gave ideal protection with its long scoop reaching well down over my shoulders and back.

'My shipmate, the late Alec McDougall – nick-named 'the Butcher' – hailed from Tarbert, Loch Fyne. At all times he wore only a common bunnet, which in bad weather he'd turn back to front, its scoop barely reaching the nape of his neck. He didn't mind being outside, as he was a keen thick black tobacco pipe-smoker, and no way would he have been allowed to smoke in the packed wheelhouse. Little did he know, until we were not long left harbour, that, on that day, he could never even have lit his pipe – the sea and spray from the mountainous waves kept pouring off the wheelhouse roof on top of us and would immediately extinguish any flame.

'There was no hope in hell of being able to warm ourselves up with even a cup of tea, as, under such stormy conditions, we would never venture below deck into the forecastle. In these days we paid little atten-tion to the environment, just respected it; never a thought given that we might be in any danger. We were used to all the freakish notions of the sea and, furthermore, we didn't know anything better. That was a ring-net fisherman's life.' [Duncan Ritchie, letter]

No steering-wheel

The *Harvest Hope* and *Star of Hope* were heading out for Loch Boisdale. It was a 'wile-lookin day', but the skippers were taking things easy. Then the *Star of Hope*'s skipper, Malcolm McGougan, called his neighbour, James Macdonald. (Malcolm, incidentally, was never heard to swear, even in the extremities of danger or despair.) 'Bliss me,' 'Googie' began, 'this is terrible – A'll need tae go intae Canna.' – 'Hoot's wrang?' James queried. 'A haena got a steerin-wheel,' was the reply. The whole wheel had disintegrated and Malcolm was reduced to steering with a stilson!

James 'stood by' him until Canna harbour was gained and the wheel could be 'patched up'. [James Macdonald]

Losing a net

Archie Paterson in the *Harvest Queen* was working three boats with Archie Graham's *Margaret Rose* and Johnny McMillan's *Maid of the Mist* and had been in Mallaig and 'got a punchin comin back again' in a south-westerly gale. They got to Eriskay just in time to catch the end of the net that one of the neighbour-boats had shot and ended up taking the catch aboard for another run across the Minch, though one of the threesome was 'lying doing nothing' at the time. 'They dinna play fair wi us,' was Archie's retrospective judgement. He took the *Harvest Queen* up to Bay Harty so that he and his crew could have a meal, because they had been unable to eat on passage across from Mallaig.

When they left again for Mallaig, the wind was 'blowing smoke' out of Bay Harty, and with all the panic to get away, the crew forgot to tie down the net. Archie had a course and a time for the crossing, but he could see the Heisgeir light and was steering by that rather than the compass and was also watching the rising sea. Then 'sma rain' came on and the lighthouse was obscured. He was now steering by compass only.

'These things happen – ye never forget them,' he recounted. 'There wir a sea struck us on the quarter and the next thing A saw wis a big curler just above her shooder. It slewed us round. A just did that wi the throttle – dead slow – an it crashed on top o the boat. It cleared everythin off the deck, an A can see her yit – she wis just lik a dog comin oot the water, shakin, an A always say, the thing that saved these ring-net boats wis the low bulwark – the water just went off her an the hatches wir all right, they stood.'

Half the net had been washed overboard, so the crew put the spring-rope to the winch and began hauling. Davie Paterson almost went over the side, but Archie's brother Dougie caught and held him. As they winched the net in, Archie noticed that the sole-rope was cut. 'Now, I don't know what cut it,' he remarked. 'It wid be terrible if it wis the propellor because we could've been wrapped up an that would've been the end.' He decided to abandon the net.

The fish-salesman at Mallaig, unknown to Archie, contacted Jim Manson, a noted local ring-net skipper, and Manson gave the *Harvest Queen* a small, shallow net designed purposely for the Fords, and would take nothing for it. It was torn from end to end, but Archie was grateful for it and he and his crew mended it over several days. That net, cryptically named 'Joe Paris', and, supplemented by two shoulders that had come off the *Rhu-na-Gal* before she was sold out of Campbeltown, saw service in the Clyde until replaced with something more suitable. [Archie Paterson]

A hold full of water

Around the winter of 1968, the *Harvest Queen* was 'working three boats' with Johnny McMillan's *Ocean Maid* and Donald McMillan's *Mairi Bhan* at Loch Boisdale. Archie Paterson, the *Harvest Queen*'s skipper, well remembered that night. The wind rose and then fell away dead-calm, but Archie knew – he could feel – that it was going to come away from the south-west again. 'It wis too quiet – ye could hear everything,' he recalled. He shouted to Donald McMillan: 'When ye get yer nets ready, we'll go away.'

So they set off for Mallaig. The *Harvest Queen* had a new, spacious wheelhouse – built by Neil McDougall, a former crewman – and a radar installed in it. There were two men below and four in the wheelhouse. Archie's brother Dugald said he would go down and take a look at the engine, but was advised, on the strength of the 'great new radar': 'Och, take yer time – we'll be in the lee o Canna within half-an-oor'.

Just then, to the annoyance of the watch, a tiny torchlight began flashing from the forecastle, so the deck lights were switched on, revealing an appalling spectacle. One of the 'bunker-lids' – a kind of manhole-cover on the deck, which, when removed, allowed a catch to be brailed on to the deck and directed through the manhole and down into the fish-hold – had worked loose and sea-water had been pouring into the hold and 'ebbing and flowing' through the manhole with the boat's motion. The catch had been spilling back out through the manhole and herring were strewn from there right aft over the top of the net. The hold was now full of herring mixed with sea-water, some of which had been leaking through a tiny hole in the forward bulkhead – the warning that the two men in the forecastle had wisely acted on.

Archie called Donald McMillan alongside in the *Mairi Bhan*, expecting to have to abandon the *Harvest Queen*, because although his crew had got the pumps going, the pumps were hardly drawing any water owing to the mass of herring; and the weight of sea-water and herring combined could have pushed out a plank and foundered the vessel. But the crisis passed and, in a constantly freshening wind, the *Harvest Queen* made Canna and lay there through the night. With daylight, she set out again for Mallaig, passing on the way a big trawler sheltering at the back of Rum.

Archie got talking in Mallaig to a Dunure skipper, Johnny Munro of the *New Dawn*, who told him that his practice, when making a passage, was to have a light high on the foremast shining on to the deck so that the watch was always aware of what was happening there. 'So that wis one lesson,' Archie admitted. Thereafter, he never made a passage without keeping the deck well-lit. He attributed that near-disaster to a mistaken faith in the value of the new radar: 'We wir comfortable in the new wheelhouse; we didna need tae look oot – we'd tae look at the screen an we could see what wis happenin.' [Archibald Paterson]

Wistaria broaches

The *Wistaria* of Maidens was almost lost one night north-west of Canna, just before Christmas 1971, when she took a lump of water on passage from the West Side to Mallaig. Hugh McPhee, who was aboard her, recalled that it wasn't a bad night 'for the kinna weather we went in'; he remembered a clear, moonlit sky. He was asleep, and 'wan o the lucky wans', because his bunk was on the lee side of the boat. The skipper himself, Billy Sloan, was on watch. The first thing Hugh heard was the engine 'revvin up' as the boat hit a lump of sea and the propeller began churning air. Then the boat 'took a scoot' off the sea and 'there wis nothin tae hold her up'. As she broached, the 'clatter' was such that 'ye'd have thought she fell on a road'. She kept going over and over. The coal-fire was extinguished when the stove-pipe dipped into the sea; the bedclothes fell out of the starboard bunks and the forecastle was a 'shambles'; light fittings inside the wheelhouse were flooded and the small wheelhouse windows stove in. She righted herself in time, a reprieve which Hugh attributed to the flat surface of the big wheelhouse striking the water. He described the freak wave as 'one o these things'; but the Sloans never returned to the Minch. [Hugh McPhee]

'It's force thirteen here the noo, pal'

The cousins Billy and Ian Gibson were crossing from Crinan to Loch Boisdale in the last *Britannia* and the *Ocean Gem* one winter's day in the late 1960s. It was a right mucky day – west-north-west wind – coming down the Sound of Mull. Just before the Heisgeir, a weather forecast came on saying that the wind was to go into the south-west and decrease to force 3 or 4. 'By Christ,' Ian remarked sceptically over the radio to the *Britannia*, 'it doesnae luck like it, Billy, cause luck intae the nor-west there.' The sky was 'jeest pure blackness'.

'Well,' Ian continued, 'it hit us when we wir aboot an oor by Canna an it's the worst day I wis ever at the sea in ma life. An eight-cylinder Gairdner gaun tae the neck an if ye slowed her doon she widnae keep her heid in the win. Yin o the crew stannin on tap o the engine-room hatch greetin. Billy … we loast sicht o yin another … the scum [spin-drift] comin aff the tap o it, ye ken? We wir speakin back an furrit tae yin another an Bert [Andrew, of the *Pathfinder*] came oan, asked us whar we wir, an I tellt him. Says I: "We're half-wey atween the Heisgeir an Boisdale." "Well,' he says, 'it's force thirteen [*sic*] here the noo, pal. We're lyin in Eynort." The worst day … ye'd tae bend doon tae luck oot the winda tae see the taps o the buggars. Och, we got a right bloody doin.' [Ian Gibson]

A freak wave

Mishaps occasionally occurred even in relatively fine weather. The *Silver Fern* of Maidens was crossing from Loch Boisdale one night with about 150 cran of herring aboard. The hold hatch-cover had been tied on and weighted with the anchor-chain. Coming on to the shoal at Heisgeir, a lump of water suddenly rose 'out of nowhere' and broke over the port side, washing the tarpaulin off, chain and all. The cover went over the side, but the lashings held and it was recovered. [Andy McCrindle]

Sleep

Sleep, in the North, as Robert Ross put it, was a 'feast or a famine'. When running across the Minch to market, it was generally possible to get below for two or three hours' sleep, weather permitting. At that time, half of the crew would stand watch, two in the wheelhouse and one on deck, which practice ensured that no harm came to the boat even should sleep overcome somebody. Fishing-boats nowadays are often steering on automatic pilot, with only one man left on watch. One of Neil Jackson's crew, Archie Carmichael, told him repeatedly, 'Any time you're on waatch, if ye feel yersel noddin get me up oot the forecastle right away, no matter where ye are or what happens; get me up an A'll take the boat if ye're noddin.'

It was remarked of Donald McDougall, the *Mairearad*'s skipper, 'Ye're aa right wi Donal, but see when he starts singin the Gaelic songs, that's the sleep comin on him!' But fishermen could go days without sleep, for, as Robert Ross remarked: 'The excitement kept ye goin.'

When Grieve Gemmell went through to fish the East Coast in 1940, there was one week the crew went to sea on Sunday and didn't get into their beds until Wednesday, between filling boats by night and landing herring by day. His father often went to bed for a couple of hours at a time; there was no alarm-clock on the boat, but without fail, 'two oors an he jeest woke up'.

In the North winter fishing, there were times when fishermen, lying at anchor for days at a time in bad weather, had ample opportunity for rest. Robert Ross recalled that the *Fionnaghal* and *Mairearad* once lay in North Bay, Barra, for nine days 'an never saw the anchor in' except when the *Fionnaghal* went to the rock for a couple of flasks of water. That was probably in mid-winter of 1951, when the McDougalls had merely seven days fishing during five weeks in the North. Neil Jackson once spent 10 consecutive days at anchor in Loch Boisdale.

It was the McDougalls' custom, Robert Ross recalled, not to linger in Mallaig over the week-end, but to leave on the Saturday, after discharging the catch, spend the night at anchor in Canna, then cross to the West Side on Sunday and have a 'good doss' that night. By waiting in Mallaig until Monday and then crossing back, a crew might 'get a doin' with weather on the passage and scarcely be fit for work on the Monday night.

When crossing the Minch in a side-roll, it was the practice among some fishermen, when turning in, to fetch a pocket-board from the fish-hold, and to jam that across the mouth of the bunk. This helped reduce the discomfort of rolling around with the boat's motion. Instead of a hold-board, some fishermen used their suitcase. The forecastle – the front section of a boat and where the accommodation was on ring-netters – was not the most comfortable place to be in a violent head-sea. In such conditions, Joe Brown recalled, some fishermen used to go into the engine-room to sleep during a Minch crossing. They'd lie – two or three of them, fully clad in oilskins and boots – on the spare slings of netting right aft at the rudder-post, with the engine blasting away in their ears; but, exhausted after a night's toil, they'd usually manage to sleep.

Airborne

The *Silver Fern* of Maidens was battering across to Barra from Oban one day in the winter of c1956. It was a coarse day – 'a dead-nebber' (the seas coming head-on) – but nothing exceptional. Most of the crew were asleep, Duncan Murdoch in one of the forward bottom bunks and Bobby, the cook from Portpatrick – rotund and weighing about 15 stone

– in the bunk above him. The boat rode a big sea, then 'jeest dropped intae a hole on the other side, lik a tide-hole', and suddenly everything in the forecastle was airborne, including Bobby, his mattress and bedding and the very bunk-boards he lay on. These boards had been removed, when the boat was beached for her spring-clean, and hadn't been nailed back in place, so when they fell, askew, they dropped on top of Duncan in the bunk below and were followed by the bedding and Bobby himself. Duncan 'wisnae too happy aboot it' at the time, but the crew later had 'a right good laugh'. [Andy McCrindle]

Mishaps and Breakdowns

In a job as elementally dangerous as fishing, it is hardly surprising that mishaps occurred from time to time, particularly before such navigational aids as radar and Decca Navigator came into use. Ringing in the North was mainly conducted close to the shore and in darkness, and the danger of hidden rocks and reefs was ever present. Fishermen who were regular in the North certainly became familiar with these dangers, but there were times when experience alone was not enough to avert an accident. It was said of several skippers that they knew every rock in the Minch ... because they'd been on them all!

A bulkhead collapses

The *Anne Marie* of Tarbert, not long launched for Hector McMillan, was steaming for Oban, fully loaded with herring from Loch Scridain in Mull. Willie 'Bull' Smith was standing aft, smoking. 'Hey, boys!' he cried. 'Dae ye no ken what's happenin on this boat? Look at the height o the stern!' John 'Doods' McDougall, deciding he needed a packet of cigarettes, went forward to fetch them and couldn't get into the forecastle. It was full of herring, and the crew quickly realised that the bulkhead – or partition – had collapsed. The boat's head was down and her stern sticking up, and with every dive she took in the swelling sea, a mass of herring slid into her bow. It was a dangerous predicament, but the *Anne Marie* was coaxed into Oban, where, however, no carpenter could be found who would do the necessary repair; so, catch unsold, the crew left Oban, passed through the Crinan Canal and back to Tarbert. The spoiled catch was sold there for fish-meal, and a local ship's carpenter, Peter 'Neacaill' Sinclair, repaired the bulkhead. It was discovered then that it had been erroneously bolted not on to the after side of the beam, but on to the forward side. [Hugh MacFarlane]

Ashore at Deer Island

The crew were 'redding', or clearing, the net one night as the *Village Belle II* of Tarbert steamed along the South Uist shore. All of a sudden she stopped dead. Neil Jackson hastily abandoned the wheel and rushed to the boat's side and, looking over, saw a rock. A searchlight was trained about the boat and her position assessed. There was plenty of water at her stern and she seemed to have grounded on a kind of natural 'slip'. Neil called his brother on the radio. 'Willie,' he said, 'what are we gonny do? Ye'll need tae come in an tow us.' After a bit of a debate, Neil remarked: 'Look at her. She's buggered. A think we may abandon ship.' – 'Ach,' his brother replied, 'gie her a bloody chance.' The *Village Maid* came in to assist and a tow-rope was thrown aboard her. With the strain of the tow-boat and the power of the grounded boat's engine combined, the *Belle* slid off the rock, apparently undamaged. In that belief, Neil stuck out the remainder of the winter fishing, but when he returned to Tarbert and had the boat slipped for inspection, there was, as he put it, 'a stone as big as ma heid stuck in her bottom'. The stone had gone through the planking and buried itself in the cement ballast. [Neil Jackson]

Hitting rocks

Neil Jackson's *Village Belle III* was leaving Loch Boisdale one night. She passed inside the island there, headed round the back of the skair and down along the shore, and was heading off to round Calvay Light, where there is a wee rock Neil had been over 'a thousand times'. Boom! The boat's arse went up in the air, but she carried on. He called his brother Willie on the radio. 'A'm jeest efter hittin a bloody rock,' he said. 'Yer erse!' Willie replied. 'Nobody hit that rock in ma life.' – 'A'm jeest efter thumpin that bloody rock,' Neil insisted, but his brother wouldn't believe him.

On they went down the coast and through Bay Harty, and just as the *Village Belle* rounded the point inside the skair there, boom! The boat was 'up in the air' again. 'A'm jeest efter hittin another rock!' he announced to his brother, who was coming up astern. Neil had been going over that rock, too, for years, 'in swells an Christ knows whit all'. This time, he realised what the problem was – it was the new boat's extra draught, or depth. She was drawing nearly 9ft. The solution too had become obvious: 'Throttle down efter that – more careful.' [Neil Jackson]

Collision with an island

The *Village Maid* and *Village Belle III* were steaming for Crinan in 'a most beautiful night' just before Christmas. As the boats approached Crinan, the fellow who was steering the *Village Belle* came down into the forecastle and said to Neil Jackson: 'Ye better come up – ye canna see yer neef [fist] in front o ye for fog.' Fog had been the last thing on Neil Jackson's mind as he relaxed below, but he went on deck and saw for himself that his crewman had not been exaggerating. Remarking to the man, 'The *Village Maid*'s up there somewhere,' Neil walked aft to the wheelhouse and lifted the microphone of the radio to call his brother. 'Where are ye?' he asked. 'A'm lyin at the quay,' Willie replied. 'This fog's jeest efter comin doon.' The night was pitch-black and the coast ahead unlit. 'Gie us a blink o yer searchlight,' Neil suggested. Moments later, a glow appeared through the murk. Neil lifted the throttle and away went the *Village Belle*, heading for the light. Crack! He had been seeing the light over the top of an intervening island just out off Crinan quay and had struck the island. The boat was examined at Crinan, found to have had her forefoot 'smashed clean off', and, having been repaired at Dickie's Boatyard in Tarbert, was ready to return North after Christmas. [Neil Jackson]

The peak in Brevig*

There is a peak in Brevig, which rises from the seabed to within two fathoms of the surface. In ordinary conditions, it didn't bother fishermen. One night the Jacksons were lying at anchor in North Bay, Barra, and a gale of wind suddenly got up. The crews lifted anchor and headed down for the shelter of Brevig, losing the wind as they went, but still having to contend with an awesome motion on the sea. Neil Jackson had the wheelhouse window open on the *Village Belle III* and, as he got down inside of the reefs, he could see the wash of the seas breaking as surf, and hear that surf above the noise of the engine. A bit further down, and he noticed that the boat was coursing on a big streak of foam, and he was smelling the tang of it, actually smelling it. He switched on the searchlight, and, in its beam, dead ahead, there it was – the peak! The boat had been over

*Known as 'The Blower'.

it hundreds of times, but there it was now, spouting water fathoms into the air. 'About turn! Ye never saw a boat gan roon as fast in yer life. Straight for it, A wis. There it wis. Ma hair stood on end. A wis a bit wary o it efter that. Ye winna believe it.' [Neil Jackson]

North of the Stuleys

'We often would spend our week-ends in Lochboisdale, South Uist. One particular Sunday we were purposely ebbed high and dry, as the day before we had scrubbed and coated the boat's bottom with anti-fouling paint. Dick, the engineer, and I were down inspecting our handiwork, and, when he was examining the propeller and rudder pintle, he said he thought he was seeing a hairline mark, like a crack, on the pintle. Neither of us could be quite sure, so we shouted up for the skipper to come down and pass his opinion. By passing a sharp knife over the mark, it could not be felt, indicating to us all that it was not a crack.

'We proceeded to sea on the Monday night and were fishing north of the Stuleys, near the entrance to Loch Eynort. The wind was strong and from the north-east. Our neighbour had shot in a wee bay that the wind was blowing right into, and they got quite a good fishing. We squared with them and boarded the herring. Someone was heard to say, "We'll need to hurry, boys – we're near in on the rocks". With the herring all in our hold, the neighbour up-throttled, and with all lights ablaze sped away out to sea. They were busy redding their net and preparing it to shoot again, therefore oblivious to what was happening aboard us.

'We had cleared our decks of herring and were washing down the decks. The skipper up-throttled to get away clear of the rocks. Suddenly we heard a loud anxious cry from one of our crew: "Hard astern, Mattha – you're heading straight for the rocks!" Hard astern we went. Then Mattha shouted: "There's somethin wrong, boys – this boat's no answerin the wheel!" We all seemed, at the one time, to realise and exclaim, each with different words: "God save 's – we've lost our rudder." – "Bloody rudder drapped off her." – "Aye, it was a crack efter all." – "Quick! Flash your neighbour, Mattha."

'All Mattha could do now was give a wee kick ahead on the engine and then a wee kick astern, and all the time the wind was blowing us further into the bay. There was no way possible to steer the boat. We aimed and flashed the Aldis lamp continuously towards our neighbour, plus all our other bright lights, and also called them continuously on the radio. Other boats, tuned in and listening to our predicament, were alas all too far away to be of any help. Our neighbour then disappeared round a headland out of our sight. We had at this time got all the long fending-off poles ready, and it now appeared only to be the back-wash from the shore that was keeping us from going aground.

'Then navigation lights appeared, coming around the headland. We all hoped it was the neighbour. Thank goodness it was. They called us by radio, asking what had happened, and it seemed an eternity until they threw us a rope and towed us out into deep water. The neighbour's searchlight was then beamed down under our stern, and, as we had guessed, the rudder had dropped off. It transpired that it was the Campbeltown boat, *Moira*, that towed us across the Minch to Mallaig, where, after discharging our catch, we went on to the local boatbuilder's slipway. Being there for three or four days, we didn't miss the opportunity to apply another couple of coats of anti-fouling. A new rudder and pintle were fitted, and back across the Minch we sailed. Our neighbour-boat all this time was fishing in company with a Campbeltown pair, *Moira* and *Rhu-na-Gal*.' [Duncan Ritchie, letter]

Half a keel missing

During the winter of 1952 or '53, the Dunure pair, *Storm Drift II* and *Summer Rose*, entered into a partnership of four boats with the Pittenweem ringers, *Hope* and *Good Design*. The *Good Design* had been at market and the other three boats were fishing on the West Side. They had started at Loch Skiport and worked their way south, ringing frequently. At 2 a.m., they reached the mouth of Loch Boisdale, and the *Summer Rose* left with 150 cran of herring to run to Oban. By this time, the *Good Design* was on her way back to the fishing grounds and rejoined the *Storm Drift* and *Hope* as they reached Barra Sound. By this time, too, Davie Wood in the *Hope* had managed to strike the rock in Eriskay Sound known to fishermen as the Politician Rock (p 177). The three boats continued south and at daylight rung 150 crans of herring in Barra Sound. The entire catch was put aboard the *Hope*, which then set off for the market at Oban, following the *Summer Rose*. Unknown to Davie Wood and his crew, who had spent the whole passage pumping water out the boat, the *Hope* had left half her keel in Eriskay Sound! Davie Wood apparently was never back in the North after that, 'he got that big a fricht when he went in an saw that he'd gone across on his own wi a hunner an fifty cran abaird an nae keel in her, ripped open'. [Iain Gemmell]

Aground with the net out

One night the *Fiona* had a good ring in one of the deep 'guts' in Loch Boisdale that the herring would filter solid into. The crew was so busy brailing that no one noticed that the tide was sweeping the squared boats into the head of the inlet. Next thing – BANG! BANG! BANG! The *Fiona* was aground, with the net out. Then the tide suddenly began to ebb, and the net was bursting between the two boats. The *Fiona*'s neighbour-boat, the *Stella Maris*, was still afloat, so the brailing operation was abandoned and the *Stella* cleared out. The *Fiona* lay there, with the net still out, until the following day, when the *Stella*'s crew, using a punt, managed to get a rope aboard her, and she was pulled off the rock. [Joe Brown]

The *Saffron* aground

In the winter of c 1952, the *Saffron* of Maidens was heading for the upper pier at North Bay to buy provisions in the shop. The crew were unfamiliar with the upper part of the inlet – normally they anchored in the lower reaches – and took the wrong side of a perched reef and ran aground. Fortunately, the boat was going dead slow, so no damage was done ... except, as Angus McCrindle admitted, to the crew's feelings! She lifted off on the rising tide, and, when they got her up to the pier, local people – who had seen their predicament – came down with scones, oatcakes and eggs. The McCrindles never forget the kindness shown to them, and ever after, when in North Bay, would have herring set aside for the islanders. [Angus McCrindle]

The *Ocean Gem* aground

As Ian Gibson quoted, 'Familiarity breeds contempt'. He was skippering the *Ocean Gem* on the West Side one night with a gale blowing from the westward. His radar had 'packed up' and he was following his cousin Billy's *Britannia III*. When he opened Calvay Light, at the mouth of Loch Boisdale, he 'jeest stemmed the licht' and put the boat on to a reef. The 'bilger'* was damaged and the *Ocean Gem* was making water. When the tide ebbed, the crew packed car tyres below the boat to protect her hull. The 55 ft *Britannia* had only about 100 feet of room to effect a rescue,

---

* Properly *bilge-piece*, a plank perhaps three times as thick as the normal planking, running fore and aft right on the turn of the bilge, on both sides of the boat, for added protection when lying over, beached.

but Billy Gibson 'came intae that bicht an he birlt it roon lik a peerie [spinning-top] an got a rope on tae us whenever she started tae move agane; an he kept the strain oan her – that kept her fae rummelin – an he goat us aff.' The *Ocean Gem* was patched up with marine-ply at Lochboisdale in the hope that that would keep her fishing until the end of the trip, but one day Ian took her out of Mallaig in a gale of wind and she only got the length of Canna when she started making a lot of water, so there was nothing for it but to take her home and have her properly repaired at Noble's boatyard in Girvan. Billy Gibson, in the meantime, teamed up with Grieve Gemmell and Willie Anderson in a threesome, and when Ian Gibson returned to the North, with the *Ocean Gem* repaired, the boats worked the rest of that season in a foursome. [Ian Gibson]

Striking a Reef in the Sound of Eriskay

'There was an incident concerning our neighbour-boat, the *Kestrel*. We were coming out of Eriskay Sound bound for Mallaig with a 40 cran quota. Eriskay Sound is very foul, and to our horror we in the *King Bird* saw her hurdle the tail-end of a reef. They assured us they were all right and carried on across to Mallaig, and we went back to Loch Boisdale. However, when the *Kestrel* got into Mallaig harbour, they had trouble manoeuvring her to a berth, and discovered the skeg* had been damaged and the rudder knocked out of position. She was beached and a temporary repair made, which kept the boat going till we got home. A permanent repair was done at Dickie's boatyard in Tarbert. It was as well that it was a small quota that night. She wasn't deeply loaded, which would account for the slight damage.' [Neil Short, letter]

A blade short

'The following year – '34 – we got some reasonable shots around the Heisgeir. On the way out, one evening, the engine started vibrating madly. When we slowed the engine and put it in neutral it appeared all right. One of the men looked over the stern and saw that one blade had come off the propeller – we only had two blades. The neighbour-boat towed us to Mallaig and my Father had to go to Glasgow for a new propeller.' [Neil Short, letter]

---

* The extension of the keel, to which the rudder-stock is attached.

An improvised engine repair

'We came to the anchorage in Dunvegan, and the following morning, on going to start the engine and lift anchor, the engine refused to start – a malfunction in the air-motor. The cause was that the spacer was broken in two. The local blacksmith couldn't help us and we telegraphed for a new spacer to be sent to Mallaig and had visions of being towed there. Then my Father had a brainwave, and from the leg of an old seaboot cut layers and laced them on the shaft of the air-motor until he had approximately the same thickness, and trimmed off the rough bits and fitted the air-motor back on the engine. This lasted to the end of the fishing. This, my second season in the North, was more successful and we did reasonably well.' [Neil Short, letter]

The *Bluebird* aground

The *Golden Dawn* was returning across the Minch from Mallaig one night, in about 1947, when her crew saw a blaze of lights off Eriskay. 'There's somethin going on here,' somebody remarked. Indeed there was – the Jacksons had rung a netful of herring and there were three boats round the net, brailing out the catch. One of these boats was Charlie Durnin's *Bluebird*, and when the 'Duke', as he was called, had taken his quota aboard, he steamed clear of the net.

Unfortunately for him, he hadn't realised that the boats had drifted inshore during the discharging operation, and he ran aground on a rock. The tide was ebbing strongly, but Danny McAulay got the *Golden Dawn*'s nose into the *Bluebird*'s bow and took her crew off. Even before the crew was taken off, the *Bluebird* had begun to tilt over with the weight of her cargo. In the darkness and prevailing confusion, the *Bluebird*'s engineer forgot to switch off the engine, and when the tide ebbed and left the engine without water for cooling, it heated up and the cylinder-head gaskets blew. The *Golden Dawn* lay off to an anchor, waiting for flood-tide, and in the meantime Eriskaymen were coming out to the stricken vessel in small boats and helping themselves to the herring.

At high water, the *Golden Dawn* pulled the *Bluebird* off the rock without incident and towed her into Lochboisdale, where she was beached and inspected. By good fortune, the part of the rock she'd struck on was slab-like and the night was calm, so, apart from a few scrape-marks along her side, she did herself no damage. The engine, however, had to be repaired, and that job had to wait until an engineer – Andy Marr of Maidens – arrived. The *Golden Dawn* fished on, in the interval, with the two other boats in the partnership, the *Frigate Bird* and *Morag Bhan*. [Francis McWhirter]

Over the reef

The crew of the *Rhu-na-Gal* had a fright on that same reef in about 1948. It was a dark, still night, but a big southerly bound was on the sea. The skipper, Hector Gilchrist, was at the wheel, with Duncan MacDonald beside him in the wheelhouse, watching the echo-meter and calling out the readings as the boat inched in towards Melvaig Head. 'Fifteen fathoms!' Dunky would call; then 12; then 10. James Macdonald was on the bow with the bulk of the crew, looking, with an Aldis lamp, for herring in the water. Just as the soundings began to be called with rather more urgency – 'Six fathom … three fathom …' – the Aldis lamp was switched back on, and rock and waving tangles could be seen dead ahead. Now Dunky was roaring, 'Three fathom – go astern!', and with that the boat's deck lights were suddenly switched on and 'wan hell of a panic' ensued. Then the reef 'blew' right below the boat's stem, and with the shock of the sudden burst of water, one of the men on the bow collapsed backwards (he was unwell at the time and returned home soon after that experience). The drama wasn't yet over, however, because the boat hadn't gone far enough astern and the next sea lifted her right over the top of the reef and into safer waters. [James Macdonald]

Standing in water

In late summer of c 1963, when James Macdonald was skippering the *Harvest Hope*, he was fishing at the Isle of Man. He beached the boat at Ramsey to effect a simple improvement to the echo-sounder's performance. Wooden slats were to be attached to the boat's bottom to divert aeration from the echo-sounding plates, thus ensuring unimpaired signals, particularly when turning the boat or working her in heavy seas. Two crew-members volunteered to do the job. They were instructed to be sure to nail the slats into the boat's frames, but they simply drove the nails into the planking, with the consequence that, during the winter fishing later that year, when the *Harvest Hope* was heading for Loch Boisdale from Mallaig in a gale of wind, the slats – unknown to the crew – were torn off and the boat began to leak through 16 nail-holes. There were three or four pairs making for the Heisgeir, but the weather so deteriorated that the decision was made to run into Canna for shelter. The crew turned into their bunks for a sleep. First man up, a few of hours later, was old Bob Morans – whose last trip North it was – and when he climbed out of his bunk he was standing up to his ankles in water. [James Macdonald]

Hurricane Hettie

This hurricane, with winds reaching 120 miles per hour, struck early on Monday morning, 14 January 1968. Two other Ayrshire boats, the Girl Margaret *(BA 30) and* Integrity *(BA 160) were hurled ashore at West Loch Tarbert, Kintyre, and were salvaged only with great difficulty.*[6]

In the winter of 1968, the *Storm Drift* was in partnership with seven other Dunure ringers, *Britannia, Fair Wind, Fair Morn, New Dawn, Valhalla, Girl Margaret*, and *Jasmine*. On one trip, the consortium was split into two units, four boats at market and four working. It was decided to go home for a week-end, so the four boats that had been at market in Oban didn't go back across the Minch, and the four boats that had been fishing that night went across from Loch Skiport to join them. From the time these loaded boats left Loch Skiport till they reached Ardnamurchan, they were awash. They discharged in Oban, but there was a big fleet there trying to get berthed for the week-end and the Crinan Canal basin was filled, so the *Fair Wind* and the *Storm Drift* were taken out to the island of Kerrera and moored to a buoy there.

While the crews were at home in Ayrshire, Hurrican Hettie struck with ferocity and both boats were cast ashore on the island. The crews had an horrific bus journey to Oban, hampered by fallen telephone wires and trees. They found that the *Storm Drift* had fallen on her side, but that the *Fair Wind* had remained upright, held in that position by a rope between her stern and the *Storm Drift*'s stern. The *Fair Wind* was merely six inches from the water's edge, but no amount of towing by two fishing boats could move her. Consequently, the rock that her keel was jammed in had to be blasted away, a task which took some three weeks. The *Storm Drift*, meantime, was placed on skids by a squad from Noble's yard in Girvan and relaunched. From where she lay, back down to the water, was reckoned at 80 ft and it took 10 days to move her that distance. Both boats were repaired and ultimately returned to the fishing, and to the North. [Iain Gemmell]

The destruction of Mitchell's Wharf

The Campbeltown fleet was lying in Castlebay at the steamer pier. Before darkness came, the crews decided to shift because the weather forecast was a bad one – south-west wind, which comes directly in on the pier. All the boats cleared out to Mitchell's Wharf, one of the old curing wharves across the bay. Five or six boats tied up to the wharf with the heaviest ropes they had, and as darkness came the crews sat listening to the wind freshening and freshening until it blew 'a howler'. Suddenly, out of the darkness, came terrible screams. When the crews scrambled up on deck, they found the *Fiona*'s crowd already up and shouting, 'The quay's away! The quay's away!' The startled crew of the *Stella Maris* 'looked intae the wind and rain – there wir nae quay!' The mooring-ropes were all leading down the way. But the crews lay there all that night, not daring to cut the ropes and run, and the moorings held. The wharf was old; too many boats had tied alongside it, and the combined weight of the boats tore it out from the rocks. [Joe Brown]

Places Remembered
. . . .

The Heisgeir

'The keepers at the Heisgeir Light often came down to speak to us, and one very quiet day we were able to go into the landing-stage and land some of the crew. We were given a conducted tour round the Light, and the view from the Lantern Room was quite unbelievable. They told us they had a pitch-and-putt course – six holes – where the sheep grazed. One of the keepers played the fiddle, and one quiet night when we were fishing we could hear him on the rock playing away. While we were fishing around Canna, the head keeper used to relay the weather conditions and any herring appearance to us through a small wireless we had on board.' [Neil Short, letter]

In spring and summer, Angus McCrindle and his crew occasionally took Sunday newspapers to the lightkeepers on the Heisgeir, if they were passing that way, heading across to Pabbay from Mallaig. They would land on the rock for perhaps an hour and gather gulls' eggs, if available. [Angus McCrindle]

Barra

'We landed some shots in Castlebay, which, during the curing season, was quite a sight with all the curing stations and a huge fleet – steam-drifters, motor-drifters, and a few ringers. Some of the piers at the curing stations, to accommodate the steam-drifters, were built out quite a distance from the gutting vats and were fitted with rails and bogies to take the full baskets to the vats. At one time there were close on thirty curing stations round the bay.' [Neil Short, letter]

'When herring-fishing around Barra, more often than not we would berth for the week-end in the peaceful, sheltered waters of North Bay. Here there was only a small stone jetty, which ebbed dry and even at high tide was still not deep enough for our boats to get alongside. We always moored in deep water with an anchor astern and our head-rope tied to a ring-bolt which was embedded in a rock. To get ashore, we'd slide down a fending-off pole on to the rock. There was always some one on board who, given a shout, would arrange the pole so that we could clamber back on board. A cran basket would be used to carry the provisions from the shop to the boat, and, with a rope attached, it would be lifted on to the deck.

'At Castlebay pier, where the majority of the fleet tied up, mooring could be a nuisance, when in stormy weather the steamer – then MacBrayne's *TSS Loch Ness* – would arrive late and the fishing boats would have to cast off to allow her alongside. With sleep paramount to the fishermen at the week-ends, this could be a blasphemous situation.' [Duncan Ritchie, letter]

Stornoway

David McNaughton remembered crossing the Minch from Gairloch in the *Nobles* and meeting up with the neighbour-boat, the *Glen Carradale*. Her skipper, Alec McBride, was exultant: 'We wir in Stornoway the day an they didn't touch us!' He had been forced in there to replenish coal and water. Talking in Gairloch with Stornoway boys of his own age in that same summer – of 1946, Davie reckoned – they told him that once the old fellows on the Lewis steam-drifters were 'away', the ring-net fleet 'wid be in Stornoway'. Actually, he was in Stornoway himself the following year – not to land herring, but only to lie the week-end – and 'naebody said anything tae us'. [David McNaughton]

The *Amalthea* and *Boy Danny* of Campbeltown were in Stornoway in 1948. The year is fixed in Duncan McArthur's memory, because the boats were new. His grandfather, James McLean – the *Amalthea*'s skipper – declined to go ashore. He had been a crewman on the naval yacht, *Iolaire*, which was taking Lewis and Harris servicemen home after the war and sank near the mouth of Stornoway harbour on New Year's morning of 1919, with the loss of 200 lives.

He had never been back to Stornoway until that day and was reliving the trauma. His mood lightened, however, when a wartime friend – a Lewisman by the name of Mackenzie, who used to visit the McLeans when in Campbeltown – came down the quay and took him ashore.

Ironically, *Amalthea* – from Greek mythology – had been the original name of the *Iolaire*, when owned by a Mr Aston Smith in Bangor, Wales. The MFV *Amalthea*, though owned by Neil McLean, bore the name of his father James's choosing. [Duncan McArthur]

'Over a long period of time, ring-netters were not welcome in Stornoway harbour. The boats out of that port always used drift-nets. However, our pair of boats ventured into Stornoway, *Acacia* and *Westering Home*. Our crews were unsure what reception we would get. When we got moored and had a look around, we were relieved to see ring-net boats from the Isle of Scalpay already berthed. That morning, we had been fishing, without success, along the Eye Peninsula, Tiumpan Head, into Broad Bay and as far north as Cellar Head. The following night, all six ringers searched from as far south as Loch Shell and as far north as we had been the previous night, with no signs of herring.

'The next morning, being a Saturday, found all six boats moored in Stornoway and intending to stay there until Monday. Only months before we came to Stornoway there had been a new Seaman's Mission opened and we were afforded all its many amenities – tea-room/snack-bar, baths/showers and reading-room, something we had never had in any other fishing port in Scotland. They held a service on the Sunday night, with all Moody and Sankey hymns. We sang our hearts out and were delighted to be served later with tea and sandwiches. While in Stornoway our two cooks had more off-time than they had ever believed possible. We were surprised, too, to find that the newsagents' were open late on Saturday nights for the sale of Sunday newspapers.' [Duncan Ritchie, letter]

Canna

Duncan McArthur described Canna as 'a lovely place' and admitted that he always hoped for a week-end there when engaged in the summer 'gannet fishings'. The fishermen played football in front of the tiny

Protestant church and enjoyed walking around the island. He once climbed to the top of the crumbly broad stac which fishermen called the 'Jyle (Jail) Hole'*, and remembered particularly the rusty iron grating on the top of the prison.

One day, when the family boat, the *Mary McLean*, was lying in Canna harbour, a middle-aged woman came down the quay. 'That's my name,' she remarked, indicating the name of the boat, which was called for Duncan's mother. She said that she lived over on Sanday – a smaller island connected to Canna by a footbridge – and invited Duncan to visit her. He went with his brother, Shamus, and they were hospitably received. Duncan wrote to Mary MacLean for years afterwards, until she was admitted to hospital in Fort William, where (in 1987) she died. [Duncan McArthur]

There is a flat-faced rock at Canna harbour, which Duncan Campbell recalled scaling on a rope, a pot of paint with him. He began painting on his by-name, 'Kemmel', but the older men in the crew were shouting at him: 'Mind an put 'CN 256' on, an never mind Kemmel!' Many years later, back at Canna in a Campbeltown trawler, the *Girl May*, and the herring-fishing just a memory, the skipper – Peterhead-born Andy Harrison – remarked to Duncan: 'By Christ, Ould Fella – there's yer name there!' – 'Aye,' Duncan replied, 'an there the boat A wis on tae – the *Enterprise*, CN 256.' [Duncan Campbell]

Tobermory

Hugh Edgar well remembered Tobermory, Mull, on a particular day – 22 November 1963. It was on that day the President of the United States of America, J F Kennedy, was assassinated in Dallas, Texas, and the *Hercules* was lying – a world away – ebbed at the stone jetty in Tobermory harbour. Tommy Ralston, in the *Nobles Again*, had earlier turned Hugh back, on his passage out, with the information that the boats' herring quotas had been secured for that night. He was working in a foursome with the *Nobles* and two other Campbeltown boats, the *Regina Maris* and *Stella Maris*, and Davie Gibson of the *Wanderer* was crewing with him on that particular trip. [Hugh Edgar]

---

* Dr John Lorne Campbell: 'On the top of a very steep rock north of the harbour there are the remains of an old eyrie-like castle called 'The Prison'. Tradition says that one of Canna's overlords was so jealous of his young wife that he kept her up there, where she died.[7]

Natives

● ● ● ● ● ● ● ● ● ●

Relations between native populations and visiting ring-net fishermen naturally varied from place to place. Local drift-net fishermen generally detested the ring-net and all that it represented (p 11), but that applied equally to fellow-islanders who had adopted ring-netting (and who in many cases were forced by intimidation to give it up).

Islanders who were not entirely dependent on fishing for their livelihood were understandably less prejudiced against the ring-net men. They were glad to receive herring in exchange for scones or eggs; if they were managing a shop, they were naturally gratified to be supplying the needs of the six-man ring-net crews.

The Gaelic language was certainly a barrier, particularly in the fishermen's dealings with the older members of island communities, whose knowledge of English would often be slight. But the Tarbert and Carradale crews in the early decades of the 20th century had some Gaelic-speakers among them, while Matthew McDougall of Carradale, who skipper-owned the Acacia, *even as late as the 1950s enjoyed enhanced relations with the Hebrideans by virtue of his being able to speak some Gaelic.*

A basket of baking

Matha McDougall of Carradale, who was the last native Gaelic-speaker in that village, often told the story of the time he went into North Bay and visited the shop to buy bread. There was wind that day and a big fleet of boats had taken shelter in the harbour. Matha asked for loaves and the shopkeeper said that he was very sorry, there were no loaves. With that, a woman came into the shop and asked in Gaelic for her bread. The shopkeeper told her, also in Gaelic, that her bread was there but to wait till the man went away. Matha, having understood the exchange, in his own Kintyre Gaelic said to the shopkeeper that he was to give the woman her bread and that he realised there wasn't enough for everybody. Thereafter, every time the *Acacia* went into North Bay to lie, the woman who had been in the shop would come down with a basket of home-baking for Matha and his crew. [Neil McDougall]

Gaelic in a shop at Lochboisdale

A story similar to the above concerns Denis McIntosh, another Carradale fisherman, and belongs to the same period, around the early 1950s. Denis, who had a 'good smattering of Gaelic', went up to the shop in Lochboisdale. There were several women in the shop speaking among themselves in Gaelic and the talk naturally turned to Denis himself and what he was wanting in the shop. He didn't say a thing until he asked for whatever it was he wanted, and he asked in Gaelic. 'Silence! They wir found oot – they wir caught!' [Archie Paterson]

Fixing an engine

Fr James Webb, referred to below, was at the time of the story, parish priest of St Brendan's, Castlebay. Many of the Campbeltown fishermen of Irish origin were practising Catholics. Fr Webb, who was born in Bristol, shortly afterwards became parish priest at Campbeltown and served there for 31 years.

When Jock McIntyre first went to the North about 1930, the Barra fishermen, who all worked drift-nets, would hardly speak to the ring-net fishermen. That hostility softened, however, when Father Webb began visiting the fishermen aboard their boats. The local fishermen also began to go aboard the ring-netters and quiz the fishermen in their limited English. On one occasion, in the late 1930s, one of the Barra fishermen had a 15-20 h.p. engine in an old boat and couldn't get the engine to work – the cylinder had burst. Jock Meenan, who later emigrated to Canada, asked the Barraman if he had a replacement cylinder. 'No, I have not,' was the rueful reply. 'We've no money.'

Jock McIntyre, in conversation later with Jock Meenan, asked him if he remembered seeing an old cylinder-block lying on the Silver Sands one Sunday they had gone a walk together. Jock Meenan confirmed that he did remember seeing it, so away they went and recovered the thing, which had indeed belonged in a 15-20 engine before it was discarded. They took it aboard Jock Meenan's boat, the *Mystical Rose*, and looked it over. Jock Meenan, who was a competent engineer, pronounced it repairable, so they serviced it, cut paper gaskets for putting over the block and had the engine going before dark.

The Barraman, Jock McIntyre said, couldn't understand how they had come by the part or what they had done to get it working again. 'Ye'd think it wis a miracle fae heaven that come doon an said: "Right – go!"' Thereafter, the ring-net fishermen experienced great generosity on Barra. [John McIntyre]

Suspicion

The Jacksons, in the *Village Maid* and *Village Belle III*, were taking herring aboard in Seal Bay and the boats were just about loaded. Neil Jackson watched another pair of boats come into the bay and shot. This was a Barra pair, not long started the ring-net. After a while the lights went on in the Barra net-boat, revealing a good ring; the herring hadn't been dried, but Neil knew they'd be dealing with a heavy catch. By that time the Tarbertmen were loaded, battening down the hatches and making a cup of tea before they would go away across the Minch to market. Neil thought the Barramen, being fresh at the job, might appreciate assistance and remarked to one of his crew, 'We'll pass close by. Ask him if he waants a hand before we go away.' The crewman duly shouted, 'Can we give ye's a hand, boys? Can we help ye's any?' No answer from the brightly-lit boats; the Barramen who had heard and looked, turned away without responding. Neil himself shouted. No answer.

Some time afterwards he was telling Calum MacKinnon of this snub. 'All we wanted tae do,' said Neil, 'wis dry the herrin up for them an then we could've left. It wis no skin off oor noses – oor boats wis loaded. A canna understand that crowd, Calum.' Calum, of course, was of the same cultural background as the Barramen and belonged to a neighbouring island, Eriskay. 'Och,' he reasoned, 'they're funny like that. They might've thought you wanted something for it.' Evidently these Barra crews, who worked out of Castlebay, didn't persevere at ring-netting. [Neil Jackson]

A kindly act

It was the winter of 1952 or '53 and the Campbeltown fleet was lying storm-bound in Castlebay. The gale was from the north-west and dry-blowing, so there was no rain. The moon was almost full in a clear sky and visibility was good by night. Some of the young Campbeltown fishermen – teenagers – heard of a dance out on the west side of Barra and decided to attend it, so they walked there from Castlebay, a distance of five or six miles. The dance was being held in a small wooden hall with a tin roof, illuminated within by Tilley lamps hung around the walls. The 'band' consisted of one man with a melodeon, but the dance went well, and when it finished the young fishermen began walking back to Castlebay.

After they had travelled a bit of the road, a cyclist overtook them and stopped and chatted for a while. Then he got on his bike again and disappeared ahead of them. The boys hadn't gone any great distance when they saw the cyclist reappear, carrying a lump of loaf and a couple of pounds of cheese. He handed them the food, saying that he had taken a thought that they might be hungry, because it had been a long night, so he had gone home and got the food. The boys sat on the roadside, around three in the morning, and hungrily devoured the bread and cheese. Tommy Ralston Jr was one of the boys. 'I never really forgot the man,' he said. 'It was a very very kindly act.'

He and his wife, Ina, visited Barra in June of 1998, saw the dance-hall – which still stands – and tried to trace that night's benefactor. He was in his late twenties back then and living with his widowed mother. Tommy was able to 'go very close to' the house in which the man lived, but despite talking with several people in the locality, including a priest, the identity of the cyclist remained a mystery. [Tommy Ralston]

Dunvegan on the Sabbath

Some Campbeltown fishermen, who were lying in Dunvegan, Skye, over a week-end, walked along a road in search of milk to buy. They saw a likely croft, with a couple of cows grazing near it, and knocked on the door of the crofthouse. The fishermen knew that the house was occupied, but no one opened the door. They later asked someone the reason and were told: 'They'll not open the door for you on a Sunday.' In fact, it was the experience of the fishermen that, on Sundays, the natives 'winna dae anythin for ye'. One other Sunday in Dunvegan, a party of fishermen took a football up to a 'wee park' close to the village and had hardly begun their game when they were told: 'Clear off – this is the Lord's Day.' [Francis McWhirter]

Blowing a horn

In all the places where bartering was conducted – at Vatersay, Aros Bay, Pooltiel, wherever – the practice of the *Lily*'s crew was to blow a horn if they had herring to offer the natives. If the night's fishing had been successful, a basket of herring would be automatically kept for barter. Aside from the dietary benefits, it was reckoned sound practice to keep in with the 'locals' in the hope that information on signs of herring might be forthcoming.

At Geary, in Loch Snizort, there were steps cut out of the cliff down to the shore, and two boys would come down and row a punt out to the *Lily* for herring. Sometimes, if the boys didn't appear, the *Lily* would be nosed into the cliff-face and Davie McNaughton and Willie 'Cully'

Galbraith would slide ashore down a pole. Of all the places that they visited in Skye, bartering herring, the house of Peter Martin in Geary was the only one into which they were invited, placed at the table and given milk and scones or a big oatcake, with the result that the Martins got as much herring as they wanted.

Some 20 years later, when Davie McNaughton was employed on the car-ferry *Arran*, he was not only recognised by a ship-mate, fair-haired Murdo – one of the two boys who came out in the punt – but also introduced immediately, by Murdo, to the pilot of the *Queen Mary*, Peter Macleod, who happened to be married to Peter Martin's daughter, Morag. To complete the postscript, the pilot later took Morag herself down to the boat to meet Davie. [David McNaughton]

Whitewashing

One summer week-end, in the late 1950s, the *Watchful* was the only boat lying in Lochboisdale. On the Saturday evening Matt Sloan was walking up the road to the telephone kiosk, when he saw a girl attempting to paint the window-frames of the cottage in which she lived with an elderly aunt. He was familiar with the girl, having spoken to her occasionally in the village bank, in which she worked, and he stopped to chat. The girl happened to mention that she and her aunt were wondering how they were going to get the cottage whitewashed. 'Have ye got the materials?' Matt enquired. 'Yes,' she replied. 'Well,' he said, 'A'll tell you something – if you've got the materials and Monday morning turns oot fine, A'll speak to the rest o the crew. A'm sure they'll be quite happy tae come up an we can do this Snowcemmin for ye.' And that's what happened.

On Monday morning, the crew appeared at the cottage and whitewashed it, the girl having borrowed sufficient brushes to allow all hands to tackle the job. The fishermen, however, thought it strange that the elderly aunt never came out and spoke to them all the time they were there. Before they left, they knocked on the door and told her that the job was finished and that the brushes had been washed out. On their way back down to the boat, one of the crew remarked: 'Funny thing – she never even offered us a cup o tea.' Just about that time, the Co-op store at the head of the pier had become 'self-service', and Matt was there shortly after the whitewashing episode. The elderly woman was also there, chattering away in Gaelic to an acquaintance, and Matt greeted her: 'Oh, morning … Nice to see you.' – 'She looked at me,' he said, 'an she gave me a kinna greeting, but that wis it. No other contact.'

He attributed her reticence to shyness, and, reflecting generally on the fishermen's relations with islanders, had this to say: 'I think, by and large, the majority of the Hebrideans were a sort of shy people. You couldn't really say they were outgoing or forthcoming in their dealings or in their conversation. I could see a difference there, right enough, latterly.' [Matt Sloan]

Angus McCrindle, another Maidens skipper, also noticed a diminution in the islanders' reserve by the time he ceased to visit the North, in 1970. But, of his earliest years there, he recalled that, 'Ye could see the curtains movin an them keekin oot at ye'. The fishermen's lack of Gaelic was, he felt, the crucial factor in their failure to be accepted by many of the islanders. (Angus McCrindle}

Invitation to a Christmas Eve ceilidh

When the *Silver Fern*, *May Queen* and *Seafarer* were lying in Loch Skiport one Christmas Eve, the postmaster's daughter appeared and invited the crews to a ceilidh, but unfortunately they couldn't accept the invitation because they were just waiting, as Andy McCrindle put it, 'for a wee lull tae get away oot an get some herrin an get home for Christmas'. Yet he considered the Barra people the friendliest of all the islanders. When he and his crew in the *Silver Fern* were lying at the stone pier at North Bay one week-end, local folk came down with potatoes and milk for them. [Andy McCrindle]

Refusal and acceptance

There were three pairs shot in Bay Harty, the *King Fisher* and the *Kittiwake*, the *King Bird* and the *Kestrel* and the *Nobles* and the *Glen Carradale*. Each got about 100 cran of herring, but the quota was only 60 cran per pair. The remainder was therefore surplus to requirements. It was a dead quiet night and the crews had been shouting over to one another, 'Are ye's needin any herrin?' The answer in each case was, 'Naw' – all the crews had more than enough aboard. Now, there was a small Eriskay boat, the *Virgin*, inshore from the ringers, and Baldy Stewart went across with the *King Bird* to this boat and hailed her crew: 'If ye's come oot alongside we'll fill yer boat wi herrin an we'll tow ye's across the Minch an discherge them for ye.' – 'Oh, no,' was the reply, 'we'll catch our own herring.'

Later in the night, the *Lily* and the *Glen Carradale* were up in Lochboisdale, almost opposite the post office, and saw a small boat lying outside. After Baldy's earlier rebuffal by the *Virgin*'s crew, the older men aboard the *Lily* were wary of approaching this crew with a like offer, so the skipper, Duncan McSporran, told young Davie McNaughton, 'Away aboord an ask them, ask everwho's aboord there if they waant herrin'. It was either that or the neighbour-boat would have to go out and dump the fish. Davie did as he'd been asked. There was an old man and a boy of about 15 aboard the boat and Davie told them that there was herring aboard one of the ringers if they would like to take them. 'Oh, yes, thank you,' was the enthusiastic response. So, the old man and the boy got 30 cran. [David McNaughton]

A crotchety harbour master

'Old Donnie (name changed) was the crotchety harbour master in Lochboisdale at the height of the ringing times. He was not known for his patience, but he had very little time for East Coast fishermen in particular. One dirty night the whole fleet was tied to the pier when one of the East Coast liners arrived. She had taken a line in her propeller, and needed to be beached. This meant that the whole fleet had to shift to let her up inside the reef that ran parallel to the pier. This was only accomplished after much roaring from old Donnie. Getting drenched in the heavy rain did not improve his temper. At last the boat got stern-first on to the beach and one of her crew, in a placatory gesture, shouted, "Wid ye like a cod, Donnie?" – "Ye can keep yer fuckin cod," screamed Donnie, then, coming quickly to his senses, he added, "A'll take a ling though."' [Tommy Ralston, letter]

The crew of the *Silver Fern* of Maidens, having gone into Lochboisdale one night to mend a 'bad net' at the quay, had an encounter with the same man. He came down and asked them what was doing, to which Andy McCrindle replied that they had torn their net and were busy mending it. Donnie's response to this was: 'A hope ye go out in the mornin an lose the bloody lot.' Apparently, fishermen would at times find the water supply at Lochboisdale shut off, an inconvenience which only the production of a half-bottle of whisky would remedy. [Andy McCrindle]

A courtship aborted

There were remarkably few amatory liaisons materialised between Hebridean girls and the visiting ring-net fishermen. Robert Ross conceded that there were many 'bonny lassies' among them, but Neil Jackson opined that they 'winna come oot till it wis dark'.

Exceptionally, one Tarbert fisherman was 'going with' a girl from Daliburgh in South Uist and was invited into the family home. 'The thing that put him off,' Robert Ross recalled, was when 'the old cailleach said "It'll not be long, Alistair, till ye'll be cutting the peats." That wis enough!' [Robert Ross]

A Barra shepherd

'One of our annual obligations was to ferry a Barra shepherd and his sheepdogs from Castlebay south towards Barra Head to desolate and exposed Mingulay, an island with high precipices where many thousands of sea-fowl nest. There is no landing-place on Mingulay and, as we carefully approached, the shepherd being our pilot, very close in to the shore he'd give a whistle and gesture to his dogs to jump over the side, and away they'd go, swimming towards the land. He'd then direct us in towards a steep, rocky part of the shoreline, obviously knowing well that the water was deep at that point. We would be standing by with fending-off poles. He'd then slide down one of the poles on to the rock, and there his faithful collies would be waiting to greet him. By means of a rope, we'd pass his heavy backpack etc. over to him. I assume he lived in one of the many deserted roofless cottages that were on the east side of the island. Quite a few hundred sheep could be seen grazing on Mingulay, so he would not be idle during his stay on the island.' [Duncan Ritchie, letter]

A Eriskayman's view of the Clyde men

'We got on very well with all the Clyde fishermen. There was always a sort of common bond between them and us. I've seen a lot of fishermen from Campbeltown and such in our forecastle, all telling great yarns. Matt Speed, who skippered the *Moira* and neighboured us, was more often in our boat than in his own boat. We had on board a crew member, Angus MacIsaac, a former merchant seaman and a very interesting man. Matt liked Angus's yarns.

'He told Matt about the time when he was a quartermaster on the *Adelaide Star* in a port in Brazil, Santos. Angus was on the gangway watch. As there was a big party on board, he refused entry to two fine-looking ladies who did not have a pass. After an argument in which one of the ladies said she was the owner, Angus, not to be outdone, said to her: 'Tell that to someone else.' Then the second officer appeared, and, 'Oh, my God, Angus, that is Lady Vestey.' Then she got through. The captain sent for Angus next day. Angus thought, this will be the sack. 'Well, Angus, here we are. I am to compliment you from none other than Lady Vestey herself for your good example as a gangway QM.' Angus had a few good yarns.

'The Clyde men thought there was nobody like Angus, whose house stands on the hill as you approach Eriskay South Harbour. In fact, it was also a guide to boats on a dark night entering the harbour. One night Angus piloted 10 modern ring-netters into the anchorage. He was on the *Moira*. The *Moira* was leading the band. A very bad night. I suppose one could say these herring days were also prosperous and happy days.' [Duncan MacInnes, letter]

Recreation

Entertainments were limited in the North, particularly in winter. Many fishermen enjoyed a long walk to escape the confinement of life aboard a small boat. Others preferred to walk only the length of a public house or hotel, which were few on the West Side, Loch Boisdale and Castlebay being the main 'watering-holes'. The cinema at Daliburgh, South Uist, was another attraction. The films, which were frequently interrupted by projector break-downs and consequent audience foot-stamping and cheering, were shown in a Nissen hut. When news of a dance would reach the fleet, the younger fishermen, particularly, would sometimes walk miles and back to attend. Football matches were played, summer and winter, with local teams, and swimming was enjoyed in summer at certain anchorages.

Mostly, however, the fishermen made their own entertainment aboard the boats. Card games, often for pennies, were popular with some crews, and musical nights were held, when the forecastle of one or other of the boats would be packed with fishermen, all of whom had to take a turn with a song or recitation. Some fishermen took musical instruments to sea with them. The simplest pastime, however, was yarning, and many fishermen liked to go aboard another boat and hear a different set of stories. The Kintyre men, if moored alongside an Ayrshire boat, would spend time there, and vice-versa. In that way, the lore of fishing circulated through the fleets.

Fishermen of a religious persuasion were sometimes able to attend church if they happened to be lying in a suitable port over the week-end. The Catholic fishermen of Campbeltown could attend Mass in the predominantly Catholic islands of South Uist, Barra and Canna, while elsewhere the Protestant majority had its spiritual needs catered for. Local congregations, both Catholic and Protestant, occasionally laid on transport to take the visitors to remoter places of worship.

The deer-hunter

Hugh MacFarlane was storm-stayed in Loch Broom one winter, at the turn of the century, waiting to get home. To pass time, he and another Tarbert fisherman, by the name of Bain, accepted an invitation to accompany a retired police sergeant, Willie Mackenzie, on a deer-poaching expedition in the locality. Mackenzie had a rifle with him, which Hugh lifted to examine. 'My God,' Hugh recalled, 'a presentation tae wan o them big lairds in Skye!' The laird's name was on the rifle, which had been given to him by his tenants. Hugh said to Mackenzie, 'A winna ask ye how ye got the rifle', and Mackenzie didn't tell him. Where Mackenzie took them, the two Tarbertmen 'never seen a deer yet, an Willie's there lik a bush-ranger, doon'. Mackenzie was a dead-shot, but every time he would fire, it was a goat he killed. Eventually, Hugh said to him: 'How are ye gonny get them doon?' – 'Down?' Mackenzie replied. 'You'll carry them, haul them, you and that other fellow, Bain.' – 'Well,' Hugh said, 'good enough – that's plenty.' [Hugh MacFarlane]

Passing the time

'You asked what we did to pass the time when not fishing. Well, most if not all boats had perhaps a pack of playing cards, a set of dominoes, a cribbage board or a draughts board. These all helped to pass the time if you were lying at anchor or kept in with bad weather. Canna was the place I remember best for putting in the time when not fishing. The boats would all be in at the pier and if the day was good a crowd would gather at the well not far along the road to have a good wash and then sit around yarning away. I found it interesting just to sit and listen.

'Then there was often a game of football played on a fairly flat field just beyond the pier. These games started off reasonably, but after a while so many men had joined in, it looked more like a game of rugby. In some boats, a number of men would be gathered telling stories of earlier times; in others there might be a card school in play. The popular game was what they called 'Solo', played for halfpennies and pennies, more or less for fun.

'I remember one breezy night in Canna listening to a 'concert' in a Campbeltown boat. One of the crew played the melodeon and was a very good singer. His favourite song was 'Tom Bowline', which he sang accompanying himself on the melodeon, and he got so carried away with himself that long before the end of the song the tears were streaming down his cheeks. I'll never forget it. A good number of men could play musical instruments such as the melodeon, the concertina, the fiddle and mandolin, etc., and a good number were very good singers, so it was fine when a group got together to give an impromptu concert.

'On a Saturday night in Mallaig, groups of men gathered here and there on the quay and could be heard singing their favourite songs. Mind you, I think being in the pub led to these various gatherings. Still, they were enjoying themselves. A favourite walk on a Sunday evening was out to Morar by road and returning by the railway.

'That was all in the summer fishing. The winter fishing was a very different matter. The weather then was very breezy in the main, and in between a fine day or two a lot of time could be spent at anchor. You could get a break and get across to Mallaig, and then on the way back to the fishing grounds be stuck in Canna for two or three days waiting for the weather to moderate. I remember going into Uskavaig in Benbecula on a Tuesday evening and having to lie at anchor there until the Friday morning before the weather moderated. It was very monotonous and frankly I was very glad when the winter fishing slackened off and we got back to home waters.' [Neil Short, letter]

Westerns and crossword puzzles

Aboard the *Watchful* and *Wistaria*, most of the crewmen read voraciously and books would be swopped with other crews whenever the opportunity arose. 'Any new books wi ye?' was a familiar cry. Rodney Sloan of the *Wistaria* was especially keen on cowboy books. Matt and Billy Sloan were 'crossword daft', and Hugh McPhee recounted: 'They wid sit daein crosswords till the Lord called them. Every paper ye got, be Jeez, there wis a bit cut oot it for the crossword – it wis usually the bit ye wanted tae read the back o!' [Hugh McPhee]

Chess

Andy McCrindle was taught to play chess by his brother-in-law, Mervyn Thorburn (p 24), who took a chess-set to sea, and 'it fairly passed the time'. Cards, reading and 'the wireless' also relieved monotony when storm-bound in remote anchorages. Andy used to go up to the hotel in Lochboisdale to freshen up in a bathtub – at a cost of 5s – after which

there would be 'a wee session in the lounge bar an back doon again'.
[Andy McCrindle]

Back with the songbook

The *Storm Drift III* was built with an unusually spacious forecastle, and
for one Saturday night's get-together there were no fewer than 26 fishermen in that forecastle, all seated and most of them 'half-jaked'. When
'Tit' Ralston went away, the Dunure crew thought that they could now
get off to their beds, but he wasn't gone five minutes till he was back,
saying, 'A wis jeest away for ma song-book'. Daylight was breaking on
the Sunday morning when the last of the revellers finally left. [Iain
Gemmell]

Psalm-singers

During the summer fishing at Skye between the Wars, when the ring-
net fleet was based at Uig, many of the fishermen would attend church
on Sunday evening and then congregate at the head of Uig quay to sing
psalms. There were many splendid singers among the Campbeltown
fishermen of that generation, not least the Blacks with their bass voices.
Archie Paterson's father, Robert, told him that 'he never heard anything
like it in his life … They started on all the old psalm tunes, ye know, on
a quiet evenin, an ye cou'na hear better anywhere, he said. Isn't that
wonderful? Ye never get that now'. [Archie Paterson]

Sunny summers

Jock McIntyre's memories of his North summers, between the Wars,
were bathed in sunshine! The fishermen went about in their bare feet,
even ashore in Canna and Lochboisdale, wearing only a vest and an old
pair of dungarees. When lying week-ends at Uskavagh, the fishermen's
only diversion was to go ashore with a gun and shoot rabbits. [John
McIntyre]

A ceilidh in Northbay

Some Carradale fishermen – all of them more or less drunk – went to a
ceilidh in the chapel hall at North Bay, Barra, one night in the 1950s
when they couldn't get to sea with bad weather. 'They had a great time
at the ceilidh,' Archie Paterson recounted, though he himself wasn't

there. 'An Denis [McIntosh] could sing a Gaelic song, but that's no' what
he did at all. He did a recitation: 'I wandered lonely as a cloud ...' Ye
never heard anything less appropriate in yer life! An he went all through
the actions. Never mind, drunk and all as they wir, they came oot an
went round the Curachan intae the inside bit an got a hundred cran on
the *Maid* [*of Morven*] an away for Mallaig.'

Denis McIntosh was a close friend of the author Naomi Mitchison,
who lived for much of the year in Carradale, and she helped him buy
his boat, the *Maid of Morven*. His neighbour at that time was Duncan
'Dunks' McDougall in the *Lily Oak*. [Archibald Paterson]

Sir Compton's House

'The 'Coddy' [John Macpherson] was a close friend of the writer, Sir
Compton Mackenzie, who had a holiday home, Suidheachan, at North
Bay. John was instrumental in our crew getting access, at week-ends, to
Sir Compton's house, where we could use the fully-stocked library and
billiard-room. We were always most grateful to him for that privilege for
a few hours at the week-ends. In such a remote region, it was a home-
from-home for us. That all happened 50 years ago.' [Duncan Ritchie,
letter]

Snooker in Canna

*John Lorne Campbell, referred to below, was the proprietor of Canna and a
distinguished folklorist and Gaelic scholar. He had, incidentally and ironically,
been active in* Comunn Iasgairean na Mara – *the Sea-Fishermen's League
– which was founded in 1933 to agitate for the restriction of steam-trawlers'
and ring-netters' operations within the Minches.*

Matt Sloan and his crew lay one week-end in Canna with the *Bairn's
Pride*, an infrequent occurrence because normally, if fishing the Canna
grounds, they would spend the week-end in Mallaig. On that occasion,
however, they had come out of Mallaig on the Friday night. It turned
out to be a very poor night, so they ran into Canna. There was still a
fresh breeze on the Saturday, so they decided they would remain there
for the week-end and cross to Loch Boisdale on the Monday. While in
Canna Harbour, John Lorne Campbell came down to the boat and was
given a meal of salt herring. Before taking his leave, he remarked: 'You're
in here for the week-end. If any of you are of a mind to come over to the

house tonight, I have a billiard-table there and no one to play with me.'
– 'Oh,' Matt replied, 'I'm quite interested in billiards, but my favourite
would be snooker.' So he went to Canna House that night, and passed
a few hours playing snooker with the laird. [Matt Sloan]

Football

When the Campbeltown boats were lying in Lochboisdale over a week-
end, the local boys might, weather permitting, come down about twelve
o'clock on a Sunday, after the church came out, and invite the young
fishermen to a game of football. They'd all travel by bus out to the
machair on the west side of the island and play their game there. When
lying in Portree, Skye, a football match could sometimes be arranged
with the local High School boys. [David McNaughton]

MacLeod's Tables

*MacLeod's Tables, on Skye, are formed by the twin flat-topped promontories of
Healaval Mhor and Healaval Bheag, the former 1,538ft in height and the latter
1,601ft. The traditional explanation of the name is that the seventh chief of
Clan MacLeod, Alasdair Crotach, entertained a Lowland nobleman on the star-
lit summit of Healaval Mhor, on which food and wine had been spread for a
banquet.*

A group of young Campbeltown fishermen – Francis McWhirter, Denis
Meenan and Cecil Finn – one Sunday climbed the Tables. A thick mist
engulfed them on the high ground and they almost blundered into a bog.
Completely baffled as to the direction to take, they began descending,
anyway, and eventually saw a young girl milking a goat on a croft.
Having explained their predicament to the bemused girl, she was able
to point them in the direction they wished to go. They found the ravine
she had described, followed that down, and got back to Dunvegan.
[Francis McWhirter]

Bagging shell-sand

In the winter-time, when lying in Castlebay, Barra, some of the fishermen would pass a Sunday by walking out to the west side of the island
and collecting shell-sand for bird-fanciers back in Campbeltown. This
sand was extra-fine and ideal as grit for linnets' and canaries' digestion.
[David McNaughton]

A dance in Benbecula

The *Moira* and *Nobles Again* ran loaded into Lochboisdale one night in a gale of wind. Having gone up to the hotel for a drink, the crews were persuaded, by one of the locals, to go to a dance in Benbecula. Having first shaved and changed into their 'week-end clothes' – blue trousers and smart jerseys – they caught a bus to Benbecula and enjoyed the dance. The catches were later discharged into a Klondyker in Loch Boisdale. [Duncan Campbell]

A train to Daliburgh

When the ring-net fleets were lying in Lochboisdale over a week-end, on Saturday night the old hands would urge the newcomers to the North to get spruced up and ready to catch the train to Daliburgh. 'This,' said James Macdonald, 'was a standing joke. The young fellas believed it; they aye fell for it.' [James Macdonald]

The pictures at Daliburgh

The first time Hugh Edgar went to 'the pictures' at Daliburgh, he walked there from Lochboisdale with a group of young fishermen. He was wearing 'fancy claes' – 'guid pair o flannels an a fancy-coloured pullover' – which his mother had given him and which, in retrospect, he admitted he 'should never've had on the boat'. He was walking on the outside of the group and fell into a ditch and ended up covered in muck 'tae the oxters'. 'Luck at the state o ye!' one of his companions remarked when they got to the picture-house. Of course, having no access to a mirror, he hadn't realised the mess he was in! The film-show was not, however, an experience he was desperate to repeat. 'Efter wan night at Daliburgh at the pictures, ye wirna too keen tae go back because it wis school forms ye wir sittin on, the same as it wis in Mallaig. It wis very much lik the films A seen in Dunure afore A went tae the sea – there wis a guy used tae come wi an ould movie-projector an set it up in the hall. It wis very much lik that – an amateur effort.' [Hugh Edgar]

Communications

Since a trip North might last six weeks or more, fishermen were naturally concerned to maintain contact with their families at home. Before the telephone came within the means of fishing families, contact was maintained by letter and postcard. Two sets of postcards, sent home from the Hebrides by fishermen, turned up during the course of research, one preserved by Mrs Madge McWhirter, Campbeltown, and the other by Mr Duncan Ritchie, Carradale, and these contain a good deal of day-to-day information. Letters had a practical value too, as a means of sending news of appearances of herring and of big fishings elsewhere. The installation of radio transmitters on fishing boats in the late 1940s enabled skippers to keep in touch with fellow-skippers over long distances and to hear, at once, of prospects and fishings elsewhere.

A birthday message

Grieve Gemmell was invariably in Lochboisdale when his wife's birthday came around on 18th December, and when he would go into the post office there to despatch a telegram, he'd begin, 'A'm in tae send ma …' The old postmistress, well knowing his business, would cut the statement short with, 'Wait and I'll tell you what you're going to put'. The message would be, as it had always been: 'MANY HAPPY RETURNS MARGARET. I LOVE YOU HONEY. GRIEVE.' [Grieve Gemmell]

'Where do you spread your wings?'

'Baldy' Stewart of the *King Bird* was friendly with the lightkeepers at the Heisgeir and if they saw any appearance of herring they'd give Baldy the tip. This was some 20 years before radio transmitters became general in fishing-boats, and the way it worked was that at a certain time every day Baldy would listen, on the 'trawler band' of an ordinary wireless set, and one of the keepers would call him on the lighthouse transmitter. The message was always preceded by the code, 'King Bird, King Bird, where do you spread your wings tonight?' [David McNaughton]

Tip-offs

Some time in October, around 1962, Tommy Ralston, skipper of the *Nobles Again*, got talking with the crew of a MacBrayne ferry in Oban and learned that herring were being taken in drift-nets at Tiree by small-boat fishermen. That evening the *Nobles* and her neighbour, the *Moira*, looked into Loch Scridain and Loch na Keal on the south-west coast of Mull. Marks of herring were seen on the echo-meter, so the crews waited until darkness and tried a ring or two, but were rewarded only with a few baskets of small herring. Other crews, working about the Coll Bank, were likewise having no success. On the strength of the news from the ferry crew, it was decided to head for Tiree, but the Campbeltown crews had been beaten to it. They saw lights ahead, and these belonged to the Manson boats – *Jessie Alice*, *Mary Manson*, *Margaret Ann*, and *Spindrift* – leaving Gott Bay loaded with herring. All, however, was not lost: there was still a fishing to be had. Tommy Ralston had the first shot and netted 180 cran. The neighbouring skipper, Neil Speed, shot next and he got 50 or 60 cran. These herring were sold at Oban and fetched about £1400, which was good money for a night's work at the time; the Mansons ran their herring to their home port of Mallaig. The fishing effort in the North, by that time, was annually concentrated on the Outer Isles, and these herring were believed to have been the first taken from the Tiree grounds since the 'Hoodie' – Robert Robertson – was active there between the Wars. [George McMillan]

When three pairs of ringers went through a narrow channel of Loch Uskevagh and into a shallow expanse of bays and islets, they found a pair of Manson boats already there and brailing herring (p 60). The Mansons had evidently been fishing in there for about a week before the other boats came on the scene. 'It was a local man told them about the place,' Duncan MacInnes recalled. 'Apparently he was getting herring dried up in the pools after the tide.'

On the night of the sudden storm, in December 1959, when the *Lady of Fatima* and *Moira* earlier came upon solid herring in Barra Sound, the *Lady of Fatima*'s skipper, Norman MacInnes, said that he was sure that the herring came into the Sound from the west, because an old fisherman and friend of his, John MacInnes of Benstack on Eriskay, 'had seen a lot of gannets and gulls way out west by Fhuda at the beginning of the week'. [Duncan MacInnes, letter]

American Forces Network

When radio transmitters were first installed in the boats, they were, of course, great novelties. When the *Regina Maris* would be making a passage, the younger men – Francis McWhirter and Denis and James 'Whitey' Meenan – would take the first watch in the wheelhouse, and spend the hours listening to the American Forces' Network, Rosemary Clooney being a particular favourite. The older men were below, turned in and oblivious to this breach of the rule, which was that the set should be tuned to the fishing 'band', or channel. In the course of the watch the boys would flick on to the fishing band from time to time to listen to the other boats, in case some one was trying to call them; but if the night was dirty, they went by the rule and kept the set tuned in on the fishing band. [Francis McWhirter]

Telephoning home

When the fleet was lying in Lochboisdale over a week-end, you could queue for hours to telephone home, because there was only one line to the mainland from there. It therefore became important to be able to go up to the telephone kiosk and book a call with the local exchange for a certain time. In the immediate post-war period, few homes had telephones and it was necessary to have made arrangements with the person you wished to contact to be at a telephone around the time the booked call would come through. [Iain Gemmell]

Francis McWhirter had no telephone at home, so his wife Madge would go to his brother John's house to receive telephone calls. Sometimes she would call him – a simpler arrangement – having been apprised earlier of the call-box number of wherever he expected to be at the week-end. He would go up to the box at a given time, say 7 or 8 o'clock on a Sunday evening, and wait until the phone rang. At Lochboisdale there would always be others waiting to call home. These inconveniences were part of the experience of fishing away from home, but the crews would always try to ensure that they were lying somewhere a telephone could be reached. [Francis McWhirter]

'From the sublime tae the ridiculous'

When Robert Ross went up to the telephone-box in Lochboisdale one night, about 1950, there was a big queue, which he joined. A Campbeltown fisherman was immediately ahead of him, 'phoning a 'bit of stuff' he'd met in Whitby, where the previous fishery had been. The man's voice was so naturally loud that Robert could hear every word of the conversation, which began with, 'How are ye doin, ma dear?' The woman had obviously asked him where he was, because the next remark was: 'We're from the sublime tae the ridiculous.' [Robert Ross]

Golden Hind

Duncan MacDonald was coming across the Minch for Oban in the *Golden Hind* one dirty night and was trying to get a link-call through. He had contacted Oban Radio, but the operator there was having difficulty catching the name of the boat. 'Would you please repeat the name of your vessel? We can't get you right. Please repeat the name of your vessel.' '*Golden Hind*!' Dunky would bawl back. This happened four or five times, and, at the finish up, Dunky roared into the microphone: 'Drake had wan o the fuckin things!' [Ian Gibson]

A perilous mission

When Andy Alexander of Maidens got word that his wife, Margie, had given birth to their first child (on 20 December 1954), he asked his chum, Andy McCrindle, to go ashore with him to the phone at Castlebay, Barra. The boats were moored, with anchors out astern, at Mitchell's Wharf, and the two men got ashore over the bows. Andy Alexander was in the *May Queen*, at that time, and Andy McCrindle in the *Silver Fern*. Each took a torch and away they went into the driving wind and rain. Andy Alexander made his phone call and the two were returning to the boats when Andy McCrindle went through an old rotten plank on the wharf. Only his outspread arms saved him from plunging below the wharf, and Andy Alexander was able to haul him out. The boats had earlier lain in North Bay for three or four days – 'aa ye could see wis the tops o the boats' masts oot the spume' – and when the wind eased, on the Saturday, had shifted to the steamer-pier at Castlebay in order to get stores and water. The crews went ashore that night, 'had their refreshment' and returned to the boats. About three o'clock in the morning, with the crews lying snug in their bunks, a gale got up from the south-west and forced them to shift across to Mitchell's Wharf, where they lay three or four days more. [Andy McCrindle]

'Have ye heard the Rangers' score?'

A Dunure crew came across from Mallaig to Loch Skiport in a gale of north-west wind one Sunday night and had just got moored to the quay and put the lights out, when, to their utter shock, out of the darkness came a voice: 'Have ye heard the Rangers' score?' The voice belonged to a son of the piermaster in Loch Skiport. He'd seen the boat's lights approaching and had made his way down to the quay to enquire about the previous day's game, the family's radio battery having gone flat. The crew later befriended that Macleod family and maintained the friendship over the years. [Iain Gemmell]

Television

In time, television penetrated the world of working fishermen. By about 1970, there was a small black and white set aboard the *Britannia* of Dunure. Jim Munro recalled leaving Mallaig one winter's day to go away for the West Side. The forecast wasn't good, but the weather was still tolerable when the *Britannia* set out. Half-way to Sleat, however, the storm broke: 'Jeest lik a clap o yer hans, away it came, a right screamer.' They were forced to run for Rum harbour and were three hours getting there, compared with the normal half-an-hour, and met the new-built square-sterned *Spes Nova* running in the opposite direction, before the wind. The *Britannia* was storm-bound for about a day-and-a-half in the Rum anchorage, and Jim recalls, as the youngest crew-member, climbing the boat's mast and turning the aerial this way and that, trying to get a picture on the television set; but it was a 'waste o time' – there was very seldom any reception in the North at that time. [Jim Munro]

Provisions

Ship's biscuits

When Willie Anderson was a boy in the *Bonito*, the boat was lying in Mallaig one day. The crew was in the forecastle and his uncle Willie said to him: 'Go up and get some ship's biscuits.' Young Willie had no idea at that time what ship's biscuits were – they are a species of hard biscuit, baked from flour, water and salt, and designed to last almost indefinitely, as a stand-by when other provisions have been depleted. He duly went to a grocer's shop in the village and returned with half-a-stone of the biscuits. His uncle, sitting engrossed in a cowboy book, took one of the biscuits, spread it with butter and absent-mindedly took a bite. At once his teeth flew out both sides of his mouth, broken, and he's shouting: 'Christ, you've ruint me, you've ruint me!' The crew were all sitting round laughing. Hard tack was never brought aboard the boat again. [William Anderson]

When the Tarbert skiff-fishermen were preparing for the North, they always ordered eight stone of biscuits at the baker's. Beside the stove, they had a specially-designed air-tight biscuit-box with a hole in it, 'an ye put in yer erm'. The biscuits would keep firm for months with the heat of the stove. The hole was covered with a disc, which was simply moved to the side and then swung itself back into place, on its nail, when the biscuits had been taken out. [Hugh MacFarlane]

When Denis Meenan's father was preparing for a trip North, a couple of dozen 'loaf-cartons' full of hard, rimmed ship-biscuits would appear in the house, and his father would immediately warn the children: 'Don't youse go near them biscuits!' But the warning had no effect, and Denis would creep along the lobby on hands and knees to filch one out of its carton. In his early years at the fishing, he was 'shipmates' with the biscuits, and no doubt found them far less desirable than when they were forbidden to him. They hung in a piece of netting above the forecastle stove to keep them crisp. [Denis Meenan]

'These biscuits were stored in a tin box under the stove, the driest spot in a wet boat. There were no sweet biscuits allowed aboard except when they were bought, as a rare treat, if some herring were sold by the cook in, say, Lochboisdale. They were sneeringly referred to by my father as 'snasters'. The only sweet treat we got as youngsters was a sneaked piece of bread thickly coated with condensed milk, and there was a row if you were caught at that!' [Tommy Ralston, letter]

Provisioning at Tarbert

The fishermen brought aboard a good stock of 'dry stores' for the North, expecting to have to replenish only the bread and butchermeat while on the fishing grounds. Every locker would be jammed with provisions and, as Robert Ross remarked, 'Ye cou'na wag a stick in the forecastle.'

Provisioning at Carradale

'The Carradale fleet, in preparing for the North, would fill the coal-bunker and invariably our victualling would be sure to include a dozen of John Paterson and Company – the local baker's – home-baked white loaves. Bread in the Hebrides was always a scarce commodity. The order too would include three or four dozen of Paterson's rimmed hard biscuits, no longer baked. The biscuits, if sealed in tins, withstood the damp atmosphere of a fishing boat, and it took a long time to penetrate and spoil them.' [Duncan Ritchie, letter]

In the North

On occasion, when 'stuck at anchor' on some remote coast, the boy-cooks would have to make do with whatever limited supplies were available – perhaps a few vegetables cooked in a pot of water with a block of margarine to produce soup. In Joe Brown's early years at the fishing with Tommy Ralston in the *Golden Fleece*, ship-biscuits, stored in tin boxes, would be carried North. These were bought in bulk from Joe Black the baker in Saddell Street. In Lochboisdale there was no shortage of mutton, and if any boat was going across the Minch to market, a list of stores would be passed aboard and the purchases made in port and brought back along with any mail that was awaiting collection. In latter years, ample provisions were carried, even meat, which was pre-cooked and rationed out to last the week in case further supplies proved difficult to obtain. [Joe Brown]

Blue mould

Angus McCrindle recalled leaving Maidens after midnight on a Sunday and lying storm-bound in Loch Skiport until a Friday, and having to cut blue mould off the last of the loaves in order to have bread to eat. Scarts were shot and cooked in a pot of soup; and after the soup had been eaten, the birds would be eaten too.

Rations

The boat was probably the *Golden Sheaf* of Maidens, and the crew had gone the best part of a week in the North without getting stored up. By the end of the week, they had been restricted to half-a-slice of bread each for breakfast, and at one sitting Jimmy Wright was stationed at the head of the table with a bread-knife, threatening to chop the fingers off any man who reached out to get an extra piece of bread. [Matt Sloan]

A sheep butchered

The family that kept the little shop at Loch Skiport would kill a sheep for fishermen, and on one occasion the crews of the *Mairearad* and *Fionnaghal* took half an animal each, butchered into haunches. The *Mairearad*'s portion was considered too fresh to eat at once, so it lay in the boat's hold for the best part of the week. The crew was running herring all week, and 'Moll' (Calum Smith) was 'kickin the sheep through the howld in the *Mairearad*, hosin it doon an takin the scales off it efter ye discherged'. By the end of the week, the crew decided they'd try a bit of it and it was excellent. 'A never ate mutton like it,' Robert Ross recalled. 'It wis well seasoned between gettin burried in the herrin an gettin hosed doon.' [Robert Ross]

Boiled herring

Herring was a staple in the fishermen's diet, particularly in earlier times before varied and extensive provisions were carried. After a night's fishing, when the neighbour-boat had gone away to market with the catch, a crew would often have a meal of boiled herring before turning in. The fish – three or four for each man – were put into the pot with their tails on, and when the tails came off in the boil that was the fish ready. Willie 'Elkie' Munro once remarked to Grieve Gemmell: 'Dae ye ever notice how, if ye have biled herrin before ye go tae yer bed, when ye get up in the mornin yer mooth feels as clean as if ye'd been cleanin yer teeth aw nicht?' Grieve began 'studying' Elkie's observation and found that he agreed with it. He could only surmise that there was something in the herring that cleansed the mouth. [Grieve Gemmell]

Salt herring

'Salt herring' are herring cured in coarse salt in small barrels, usually called 'kits' or 'firkins'. They were a winter food, once much relished, and a stock would be salted down both for home and boat.

'I recall being aboard a Tarbert boat in Lochboisdale one Saturday night. The men had been in the hotel bar, and were feeling no pain. Whisky hunger came on them, and someone suggested a feed of salt herring and tatties. It was common to boil the potatoes and the herring in the same pot, as the potatoes took some of the excess salt from the herring. The huge soup pot was taken out into the hold where the kit of herring and the bag of potatoes were stored, was filled, and water was added from the tap in the forecastle. The primus had been lit and the pot was put on. When the pot started to boil, the lid was removed. I then saw that the potatoes had not been washed at all, and the bubbling liquid now resembled the photographs I had seen of the boiling mud in Rotorua in New Zealand. They were eaten and, yes, I had my share. 'Splendid herrin, boy, eh?' was the only comment from my busy friends.' [Tommy Ralston, letter]

White fish

White fish were frequently caught in ring-nets along with herring. Angus McCrindle once took five boxes of cod from Billy's Bicht along with herring, and Cecil Finn recalled that, when ringing repeatedly in daylight at Moonen Bay, a good many turbot – a prized member of the flatfish family – came up in the nets. In another of the Skye lochs, Poolteil, a basket of beautiful big 'flukes' (plaice) and lemon sole in a single haul of the ring-net was not exceptional. On one occasion, fishing at the south end of Raasay, off a disued ironstone-mine, the *Lily* of Campbeltown rung three huge plaice. The *Lily*'s crew kept one for themselves, which, cut into six pieces, provided a substantial 'rasher' for each man; another was given to the neighbouring crew, and the third went to a friend in Portree, Davie Sinclair. A small East Coast boat regularly worked a seine-net in that area, and, as Davie McNaughton speculated: 'God knows hoot he wis gettin.'

Matt Sloan recounted a curious incident which took place in Barra Sound. Two Ayrshire boats, the *Elizmor* and the *Seafarer*, shot their nets virtually back to back, one hauling west and the other east, and one net contained skate mixed with the herring, while the other contained flukes.

When the *Britannia* and *Fairwind* were leaving Lochboisdale one day, the *Britannia*'s crew saw a mark on the echo-meter and shot. There were no herring in the net, but 30 boxes of good-sized cod surfaced. These fish were stowed in the hold, but, when a netful of herring was hauled that night, the cod were dumped to accommodate the more valuable fish. Jim Munro further recalled that when the hatch-boards were removed at market, there were sometimes flatfish flapping around on top of a catch of herring. Still alive, these were often flung overboard, so that, as he remarked, 'There two or three flounders ended up in Mallaig that sterted off on the West Side.'

Otter-trawling

Some Ayrshire crews kept a small otter-trawl and trawl-boards to drag for white-fish. There was no commercial interest in this pursuit. It was largely recreational, with the bonus of a meal of flatfish if the drag were productive. Angus McCrindle lifted two boxes of 'lovely big flounders' from Sandray Sound one Saturday afternoon. The crew had a feed of the fish themselves and gave away the rest. A Lossiemouth seine-net skipper, whose nick-name was 'Boysie', regularly came to Barra Sound in the week before Christmas. He would haul his net twice over the ground to clear the wrack and after he had done that he would get the flatfish.

Matt Sloan, in the *Bairn's Pride*, had a short tow with his otter-trawl inside Muldonich one Friday night, and lifted a good bag of flatfish, after his brother had gone to market in the neighbour-boat. He also tried ottering in Loch Pooltiel, but, though there were flukes in the net, the crew couldn't get them out because the net was absolutely choked with seaweed, a consequence, Matt reckoned, of the ground's being 'too exposed'. A tow on the north side of Pooltiel yielded only dogfish. [Matt Sloan]

Flounder sauce

This customary Saturday night dish consisted of fish – preferably flatfish – descaled and with the heads, tails and fins removed, first fried and then stewed in a frying-pan with masses of onions in a sauce made with diluted 'Carnation' tinned milk. 'The sauce wis better than the fish. It wis a delight that. Two loafs awa, jeest dippin the breid in the sauce.' [Hugh Edgar]

Shooting for the pot

All the Tarbert boats carried guns and two or three boxes of cartridges wherever they went, for the shooting of seabirds was part of the culture of Tarbert and earned the fishermen there the collective nick-name of 'Dookers'. 'Dooker' was the local name for the guilliemot and 'dooker soup' was relished both at sea and ashore. Shags and cormorants – together known as 'scarts' – and the great northern diver, or 'moorlach', were also shot. 'If ye'd see a moorlach or that in the North, the gun wis up right away,' Robert Ross recalled. When Tarbertman Ronnie Johnson was crewing aboard the *Silver Fern* of Maidens in the 1950s, the

Ayrshiremen were subjected to his scart stew; but these birds weren't shot – they'd been 'fankled up' in the wide wings of the net and had their necks wrung. The birds weren't exactly to Andy McCrindle's taste; he found them 'awfu strong-flavoured'. Some of the Campbeltown fishermen shot rabbits on the Outer Isles, as much perhaps to pass the time as to fill the pot, and certain Mallaig crews were reputed to go ashore on Rum with a rifle to shoot deer.

Gull eggs

Gull eggs were collected for food around May. There was a rock at the mouth of Loch Eynort and the Tarbert fishermen would go ashore there on a quiet day, putting the boat's nose into the rocks and jumping ashore. Once ashore, they would break all the eggs in the nests they intended gathering from, and when they returned the following day, would help themselves to two or three dozen of the freshly-laid eggs, which were used only in pancakes and the like. [Robert Ross]

The Ayrshire fishermen were given permission, by John Lorne Campbell, the proprietor of Canna, to gather gull eggs on the island. The eggs were got mostly on the north-west side of the island, but on a Sunday some of the men would walk round the island, for the sake of the exercise. If they found a pool of water close to a nesting site, they would put the eggs, which they carried in their jerseys, into the water, and if the eggs floated they were judged to be clocking and flung away. But a team of Ayrshire fishermen came down from the pub at Gairloch one night and decided to cook the gull eggs that had been gathered earlier on Longa Island. 'Half o them wis cloakin – they ate them jeest the same!' [Angus McCrindle]

A mess

'I am reminded of the time we went for gulls' eggs on the Stuley Islands. Several of us scrambled ashore over the stem, and set off on the hunt. I had the foresight to realise that I would need something in which to carry the eggs back, so had taken with me one of my seaboot stockings. This had been knitted by my mother from the black and white oiled wool. The stocking was soon filled with as many eggs as I thought it would hold, and I set off back to the boat. En route, I fell into a hole which was hidden by the heather, and most of the eggs were smashed. What a mess.' [Tommy Ralston, letter]

Chastisement, no chastisement

The pursuit of gulls' eggs was the cause of a trio of teenaged Ayrshire fishermen getting into bother in Gairloch. One was from the *Virginia*, one from the *Veronica* and the other from either the *Margarita* or *Senorita*, and all were about 15 years old. One Saturday afternoon, they borrowed a punt from the harbourmaster at Gairloch and set off rowing down the loch to gather eggs on the island of Longa, some four miles distant at the mouth of the loch.

The afternoon was fine, but with evening a wind sprang up and freshened, and the boys found themselves rowing back to harbour against a stiff offshore breeze. At dusk, the father of one of the boys, becoming anxious, made enquiries and discovered where they had gone. One of the boats was cast off from the pier and headed down the loch to search for the boys. They were spotted about a quarter-of-a-mile to windward of Longa, making little headway with the oars. A rope was thrown to them and it was suggested that they come aboard. The boys, however, had no desire for close contact with their seniors at that stage and elected to remain in the punt. So, the punt was hauled close up to stern of the boat, on the starboard quarter, where, for the entire trip back up the loch, the luckless boys were subjected to the fumes and spray from the wet-exhaust, so that by the time they arrived at the pier, they were soaked.

They wanted to let go the punt and go their own way with it, but the skipper of the boat – who was also the father of one of them – insisted that they come on board the boat. His son was the first aboard and was immediately cuffed about the ears. 'Noo, that's what you get,' his father said to him. 'Go away below an get changed an get washed an get intae yer bed.' The father of the second boy merely remarked to him: 'Boy, ye're soakin. Come on aboard and go an get washed an dried and have a bite tae eat.' The man's leniency having been questioned by the first father, he answered: 'The boy's had enough punishment. Naw, naw – away ye go, son.' The third boy out of the punt also escaped chastisement, and so ended the ill-fated egg-gathering expedition. [Matt Sloan]

Digging potatoes

Duncan Ritchie well remembered his first meeting with North Bay's only shopkeeper, John Macpherson, better known as the 'Coddy'. Duncan gave him the shopping-list and he laid each item on the counter, tallied the cost and then told Duncan to put everything into a cardboard carton he'd handed him. Duncan stood waiting for the 'Coddy' to weigh out the potatoes that were on the list, but instead was handed a *graip* (garden-fork) and a strong paper bag and told to come outside, where the 'Coddy' instructed him to lay the box of provisions on a seat and dig the fill of the bag out of the shopkeeper's lazy-beds. 'He left me digging and still baffled,' said Duncan, 'and returned to the shop. He must have known, as the bag never went on to any scales, what the full bag of potatoes would weigh. However, I left the graip back at the shop door, checked the list and found that he had, in fact, charged for the potatoes ... Over the years, I had often to call at the 'Coddy's' for provisions, and I knew just to ask him for a paper poke, lift the garden-graip and go, sometimes for quite a distance, to fill the bag with potatoes. Barra is a rocky, barren island, with little soil to grow vegetables. What soil that could be gathered, plus seaweed, was taken and laid out on long narrow strips, sufficient to grow drills of potatoes and called 'lazy-beds''. [Duncan Ritchie, letter]

Steak and Kidney pie

'In any of the island piers that we would be going alongside – this was when I was the cook – I would first enquire where was the nearest bake-house. On being told, I'd make a beeline for it, armed with a good puckle herring. If we had no fresh herring, I'd take some salt herring from the boat's own barrel. Herring, in any shape or form, was considered the food of the Gods to the islanders. I'd make myself known to the baker, as over the years I had learned that the bakers always had a drawer where they kept ready pastry for rolling out and putting on top of steak and kidney pies. Over the years, on a Sunday, I often made a steak pie. This was greatly appreciated by the crew, with the highest praise for the puff pastry. The bakers would just say, 'At any time, my boy, just help yourself to a daud o pastry'. I never ever disclosed my source of pastry.' [Duncan Ritchie, letter]

Clootie Dumpling

'Another of my delicacies. Usually every other week I would make a 4lb Clootie Dumpling. I'd serve it as a sweet with heated tinned custard for Sunday dinner, and there was still ample to have later, fried with bacon and egg. We all preferred it fried. Being many weeks away from home, these tasty treats were very much appreciated.' [Duncan Ritchie, letter]

Burnt to a cinder

It was the winter of 1945 or '46 and it came away a wild day. The Campbeltown boats ran into North Bay and were there a week with weather – 'it wis jeest blowin smoke.' A pole on to the rocks from the boat's bow was the only means of getting ashore. Some of the boys went ashore and began walking to Bruernish for provisions. After a time, they saw a small road-lorry approaching and the driver stopped and offered them a lift into Castlebay, saying that he'd be returning at a certain time. In Castlebay the boys bought butchermeat, including a big roast, costing 12s 6d, for the *Nobles'* crew's Sunday dinner – a luxury indeed. The Campbeltown boys were duly collected by the lorry-driver and dropped off at North Bay. There was no fresh herring aboard the boats, but the driver was given a good rasher of salt herring for his services.

By this time the wind had eased, so the boats were able to get up to Lochboisdale on Saturday morning. That afternoon, the young cook, Archie Campbell, was told: 'Ye'd better put the roast on an we'll haev it cowld for wir dinner.' This Archie did. On the following morning, big Bobby McMillan was cooking the breakfast – the rest of the crew always took a turn at making the breakfast on a Sunday, to give the boy a break – and when he opened the oven door to put the bacon in, there was this wee cinder sitting in the oven! Everyone had forgotten about the roast and, being winter, the fire had been kept going all night. Not a word was said to Archie. He was given his breakfast, and a little later a couple of crew-members mentioned casually that they weren't having much to eat because they were waiting for the roast. Archie had the fork half-way to his mouth when the realisation struck him that he hadn't removed the roast from the oven! [David McNaughton]

Out of provisions

There were four pairs of ring-net crews stormbound in the Kettle Drum and they all ran out of provisions after several days. Baldy Stewart decided that he would try to take the *Boy Danny* to the jetty in Loch Skiport. That accomplished – not without difficulty – some of the fishermen went to a house, which had a 15 hundredweight ex-Army truck standing outside, and asked for a lift to Lochboisdale. When they got there, they loaded up with stores, which they later distributed among the boats – including a pair from the Isle of Man and another from Whitby – going alongside in the gale and just throwing the stuff aboard. [Duncan McArthur]

A Christmas dinner in Loch Maddy

One of Peter McDougall's most vivid memories of the North was the Christmas dinner he had aboard the *Mairearad* lying at anchor in Loch Maddy in a howling gale of wind. It was Christmas Day of 1956 and he was 15 years old and on his first winter trip North in the family boat. The meal, as he remembered it, consisted of corned beef and potatoes followed by tinned peaches and cream. As well as the neighbour-boat, the *Fionnaghal,* there was a Girvan pair – Andy 'Tarry' McCrindle's *Aliped* and Campbell McCreath's *Erica* – also lying in Loch Maddy. At that time, the Tarbert boats didn't go home for Christmas – New Year was their traditional break – but a couple of years later it became the norm for the market to close over the Christmas period, and the choice of working or not was removed from the fishermen. [Peter McDougall]

Christmas dinner in the lee of the Heisgeir

The Sloans used to go home for Christmas and fish over New Year. The *Wistaria* and *Watchful* were homeward bound across the Minch one Christmas Day in a gale of north-west wind. Cooking, in such conditions, would have been difficult, to say the least, so Christmas dinner on the *Wistaria* was a cup of tea and a ham sandwich in the lee of the Heisgeir, before the boats ran for Ardnamurchan. When they finally reached Crinan, it was to discover that the lock-keeper was unwilling to open the gate owing to the motion on the sea, so there was nothing for it but to run back across the Minch to Loch Skiport. Hugh McPhee also spent a New Year's Day on the West Side, aboard the *Wistaria*. When she came alongside the *Watchful,* in Shepherd's Bicht, Billy Sloan's greeting to his brother Matt was: 'A happy New Year – did ye see anythin in Skiport?' It was business as usual! [Hugh McPhee]

'Tit's' Christmas duck

It was December, and one of the Campbeltown crews had bought a duck for the Christmas dinner that would be eaten in the North, far from home. The skipper, Tommy 'Tit' Ralston, had a dram in him on the Saturday night and was addressing, in solemn tones, the duck that was sitting on the forecastle table. 'Now,' he instructed, 'you'll take off an ye'll go tae Skiport; ye'll fly doon all the bights an ye'll come an report tae me on Monday mornin if ye see any herrin in the bights.' In the end, the crew got so attached to the bird they hadn't the heart to kill it, and let it go. [Robert Ross]

The above story, with its happy ending, may be preferred, but the following account is the authentic one.

'The duck! Well, we were lying in Lochboisdale one weekend, and on the Sunday morning the old man sent me off out the Daliburgh road. 'Ye'll get a duck fae MacLellan, the boots at the hotel. He steys oot near Daliburgh . That'll be oor Christmas dinner.' This was when we fished over Christmas, and went home for New Year. Anyway, off I goes out the road to Daliburgh. That must be just about the most dreary walk in the world, featureless and devoid of shelter of any kind from the wind that always seems to blow there.

'After several tries, I got the right house. 'Come in,' was the call but I could see a distinct lack of understanding when I explained that I was here to collect the duck. Mr MacLellan went out to the back of the house and reappeared with a duck. A live one! I had no recourse but to stuff this unfortunate bird inside my boiler suit and set off, with its head peering around just below my chin, on the road back to Lochboisdale.

'It was put in the fore end of the hold and fed on bread and became, of course, a pet. As Christmas approached, everyone avoided the subject of what would happen to it. A sparse feed for six men it would have been anyway. We got a good ring of herring in Skiport a few nights later, and spirits were high. Oban and home for New Year, was the plan. As we started brailing aboard the *Golden Fleece*, herring were flopping over the hold boards and were landing around this poor bird. I am ashamed to confess that in the heat of the moment, I jumped down and cut its head off. I sat aft as we went through the Sound of Mull the following morning and tried my best to pluck the duck but when we got into Oban it was agreed that no one would eat it, so it was consigned to a watery grave!' [Tommy Ralston, letter]

Stiùrag

A Tarbert crew was in the North and an old fellow called Calum 'Sgeig' was making porridge. One of the others checked him – 'Calum, ye're puttin too much meal in the porridge' – to which Calum replied: 'Non o yer damned stiùrag here!' *Stiùrag* – pronounced 'shtoorag' – was meal and water mixed as a drink, and Calum – who 'got married up there an stayed' – had no intention of cooking a watery porridge. [Hugh MacFarlane]

A box of soap

Hygiene was not a major element in the lives of ring-net fishermen, for most of whom a wash and a shave would be their lot until they returned home and were able to have a bath.

Once, in Loch Skiport, the steamer *Loch Carron* came in, berthed, and began discharging a cargo. Some of the fishermen were watching this activity and saw a box fall out of a sling and drop into the harbour. The steamer's crew appeared quite unconcerned, and when two of the young Ayrshire fishermen questioned someone on the steamer, they were told that the loss would be covered by insurance. The boys got a life-raft from one of the fishing-boats, paddled round to the spot, and retrieved the box. It was found to contain 'Lux' toilet-soap, which kept the fleet supplied for years. [Iain Gemmell]

Tobacco

At a time when most of the adult population – and certainly most fishermen – smoked, maintenance of the tobacco habit was a constant anxiety. Most smokers took a stock of cigarettes with them to the North, perhaps two or three cartons; but Archie McDougall in the *Fionnaghal* would have about 10 cartons of Woodbine in his bed. 'A knew exactly where they wir,' Robert Ross confessed. 'A could put ma hand in wi ma eyes shut!' Joe Brown, who wasn't himself a smoker, recalled that when lying, perhaps at Eriskay, and the 'fag situation' was becoming perilous, the anchor would be lifted and the boat taken up to Lochboisdale so that cigarettes could be bought; but, as Joe said, 'there winna be a mention o grub'. There were times when the stock of cigarettes would run out and fishermen were reduced to rolling and smoking strange substitutes. 'Aleca' McDougall of Carradale was reputed to have smoked 'oose', or dusty fluff, gathered from his pockets,[8] while the characters in the following story resorted to tea-leaves.

Smoking tea-leaves

When Henry Martin was in the North with the *Margaret Hamilton*, just after the Second World War, she was storm-bound in a loch north of Harris for a 'wheen o days'. The crew's cigarettes ran out and the men resorted to smoking dried tea-leaves. Henry, who had given up smoking after being poisoned by a plateful of mince aboard the *Maureen* at

Inveraray, and who had maintained his abstinence owing to the post-war scarcity of tobacco, was disgusted by the stink of the smouldering tea and complained to his shipmates: 'God, I wid stop it before A could dae a thing lik that!' Some of them reminded him that he had cigarettes below his bunk, and he acknowledged that he had indeed a supply there, secreted, long before, as a stand-by in case his resolution faltered. He lifted the mattress at the head of his bunk and removed an 'Elastoplast' tin, which he opened. The tin was rusty and the cigarettes inside it were stained with the rust. He put the tin on the table and remarked: 'There ye are – dae whoot ye like wi them.' A row threatened to break out among the desperate crew, but, in the end, the cigarettes were divided equally, and, 'roost or nae roost, they smoked them!' [Henry Martin]

Alcohol
· · · · · · · · · ·

Some fishermen didn't drink at all, while others couldn't get enough of the stuff. One Ayrshire skipper, indeed, was alleged to have 'optics' at the back of his wheelhouse, with a bottle of whisky, a bottle of gin and a bottle of rum at hand. In ports and anchorages where there was a licensed hotel or public-house, the drinkers would gather there, while the younger crew-members or tee-totallers found other means of passing time.

'Magic' whisky

The effects of strong liquor aren't always harmful, as this story from Hugh MacFarlane will demonstrate. He described the whisky as 'magic'; it must have been of the illicit variety and very potent. He was drift-netting in Loch Broom in November of c. 1905. The crew had filled the skiff with herring in the quiet waters of the sound between Tanera More and Tanera Beg, but when they came out into the loch they caught the full force of a gale and the boat almost turned 'upside-doon'. Fortunately, the sail was set for fair wind and was only 'hingin fae the boat', so the belly of it, which had struck below the boat's bend, kept the sea from filling and capsizing the vessel. Once she'd righted herself, the sail was lowered at once and the boat 'run straight before it'. They got into the lee of Tanera Beg – not without first almost striking the rocks as they tried to turn into the sound – and lay the night there. The crew wasn't able to light a fire – 'everything wis soakin below' – but contrived to prepare a meal. Daylight came and the gale was still blowing, but at about 8 a.m. it was decided to run for Ullapool. All the reefs were taken in on the sail, they managed round the point, and the wind – which was north-west and fair – took them into Ullapool.

They'd had nothing to eat since 4 p.m. the previous day. The herring had been sold, at 14s a cran, and while the crew was waiting to begin discharging them, one of them said: 'Come on an get yer mornin afore we start.' They all went up to the Royal Hotel, so exhausted they could 'hardly walk up the brae'. 'Now,' said the crewman whose idea it was, addressing a man by the name of Macleod who was tending the bar, 'we're waantin four o yer best glesses o whisky.' – 'Well,' Macleod replied, 'I'll give you that, but you'll not drink any more.' He put a glass in front of each of them. The whisky having been consumed, one of the Tarbertmen asked if they could have the same again. 'Oh, no,' said Macleod, 'I couldn't do that. A fill of that could only spoil you. I'll tell you what I'll do with you. I'll give you one half apiece.' First, however, each man had to make a promise, but the nature of that promise was unclear – perhaps they were sworn to secrecy as to the source of the stuff. Anyway, the whisky put new life into them and they emptied the boat and sorted their nets before they cooked a meal. 'Wi a gless an a half o whisky. It must've been good. He never said yit.' [Hugh MacFarlane]

No more dancing

Three pairs of Campbeltown ringers were based at Ullapool while fishing around the Summer Isles in the spring of 1946. One Saturday, a fishermen's football team played a team from the crew of a naval ship which was lying in Loch Broom. Afterwards, a dance was held in the church hall, but many of the fishermen were drunk by this time and some of them 'went amock'. On the following day, a big notice – signed by the minister – was seen displayed at the hall: 'THERE WILL BE NO MORE DANCING IN THIS HALL.' [Duncan McArthur]

'Sell me tae!'

A Campbeltown crew was in Mallaig with herring on a Saturday morning and stayed there the week-end. The skipper and one of his sons went up to a pub and imbibed enthusiastically. On their way back to the boat, they noticed a fish-auction in progress. Long-liners had landed catches of cod and ling and each catch was heaped on the quay with the buyers round about it bidding. As father and son made their hen-toed way to the auction, the son slipped on fish-slime and slid on his back into a pile of fish. At once, he threw out an arm and shouted: 'Sell me tae!' [Archie Paterson]

Cracked ribs

A pair of Campbeltown boats were in Mallaig one week-end and one of the skippers 'had a good dram on the Saturday night' and fell and struck his ribs on the boat's hatch getting back aboard. The pair returned across the Minch and were lying in Barra Sound ready to begin fishing, but the injured skipper was in agony and it was decided to go up to Lochboisdale for medical advice. The doctor from Daliburgh, having completed his examination aboard the boat, confided in the skipper's brother, without realising the relationship between the men: 'If that man was in the Army, I would say he was malingering.' No treatment was offered and the skipper suffered until the following week-end when, back in Campbeltown, he went straight to his own doctor and was diagnosed as having three broken ribs. His bitter comment was: 'A'm sure A've known better horse-doctors than that fellow in Daliburgh.' [Archie Graham]

'Well done, Dougie ...'

When Robert Paterson, the father of Archie and Dougie Paterson in the *Harvest Queen*, died in December 1959, the two brothers went home to Carradale from Loch Skiport for the funeral. The arrangement was that the boat would be left at Lochboisdale and the remaining crew temporarily join the neighbour-boats, two on the *Maid of the Mist* and two on the *Nobles Again*. That arrangement didn't work out, however, and the *Harvest Queen* ended up with 106 cran aboard and running for Mallaig with a character from Campbeltown at the wheel. He shall be identified only as Dougie, and Dougie was blithely steering for the Sound of the Heisgeir until one of the Sloan brothers shouted on the radio, wondering what boat was ahead and where she was going. The course was accordingly altered and the *Harvest Queen* reached Mallaig and discharged her catch, which contained a good deal of mackerel mixed through the herring. Now, mackerel was classed as 'stoker', in other words whatever money it realised didn't go through the account-books but passed straight into the hands of the crew. Dougie got drunk with his share and spent the night raving in his bunk. His shipmates were to hear the phrase, 'And the Good Man said, 'Well done, Dougie, thou good and faithful servant", countless thousands of times that night until one of them, in sleepless desperation, went for the Police.

At 7 o'clock the following morning, the *Harvest Queen* set off back across the Minch astern of the *Golden Hind* and the *Moira*, with Dougie, still well-oiled, at the helm. It was a dirty day and when the boats were 'square with Canna', one of the crew shouted out the forecastle hatch to Dougie, 'Turn this boat back! You're not givin this boat a bad name!' – 'Go you tae fuck!' was Dougie's emphatic response. He carried on defiantly and only turned when the *Golden Hind* turned. All three boats ran into Canna for shelter and the *Harvest Queen* ended up moored alongside the *Moira*, whose crew was in the boat's hold, putting a new bag into a net … and that's where the Carradale crew spent the night, clear of Dougie, who had no bad in him but was exceedingly troublesome and needed constant watching. [Neil McDougall]

Nature
· · · · · · · · · ·

The Canna stag

A Campbeltown boat, the Robertsons' *Pioneer*, was anchored at Canna on a poor night. While the crew was sitting in the forecastle they became conscious of a persistent tapping coming from outside. One of them finally said to Andrew 'Knuckler' Robertson, who was seated nearest the hatch: 'Andrew, will ye go up an see whoot the hell that is alongside?' – 'Ach, it'll be naethin,' Andrew replied, nervously. 'Go up an see,' the older man insisted. 'Take the winky up wi ye an haev a look ower the side an see whoot the hell it is.' Andrew, being uncommonly superstitious, even for a fisherman, with great reluctance lit the winky and went up on deck with it. Minutes later the crew heard a terrified squeal from the deck and the repeated cry: 'It's the Devil!' It was a big stag, supposed to have been swimming from Rum to Canna, and which, on reaching the boat, had begun going along the side of the obstacle, its antlers clattering against the planking. Andrew, however, knew nothing of this when he looked over the side with the light and saw the big hairy face with horns. [David McNaughton]

Dogfish

Dogfish fed voraciously on herring, and where large shoals of dogfish were, trouble often lay in store for fishermen. These small sharks, in their efforts to get at the herring trapped en masse behind the wall of netting, would routinely destroy the bags of ring-nets when boats were 'squared' and taking a catch aboard. Neil Jackson saw one bag 'eaten' by dogfish at the Heisgeir. 'We'll go in an put in a new top bag,' his father said. They removed the damaged bag and replaced it with 'a brand new tarry top sling – sixty yerds and twinty score'. They went out again and shot and filled the net, but, before they could get the herring aboard, that bag was also destroyed. The next day, the crew removed that bag too, but it couldn't be mended, 'there wir that many holes in it'. As the herring were being brailed aboard, the sweeping beam of the Heisgeir lighthouse would illumine the 'golden eyes' of the dogfish 'lookin up at ye [and] ye'd be frightened ye wid tummle over the side'. [Neil Jackson]

Robert Ross explained that the tarred bag was so hard, the dogfish would 'get a grip o it [and] chow a hole through it'. He recalled Pat McKay, a Campbeltown skipper, one year when dogfish were a plague in the Showls of Loch Fyne, taking a basket of herring to the stern of the boat and throwing the fish over the side, feeding the dogs and keeping them clear of the bag while his crew 'wir brailin as hard as they could'. Pat remarked that he was 'lik somebody feedin chickens.' [Robert Ross]

Rats

In the first winter that the Sloans had the *Bairn's Pride*, they were fishing Loch Scridain and Loch na Keal on the west side of Mull. The wind blew hard one day and the boats went into Bunessan and tied alongside a stone quay. In the construction of the quay no mortar at all had been used and there were gaps between the stones. Somebody later asked the crew if they'd seen any rats there, remarking that it was 'a famous place for rats'.

Later in the week, the Sloans left Loch Scridain, crossed to the West Side and went into Loch Boisdale on the Saturday morning. After the crew had eaten breakfast, one of them, Andy Alexander, opened the door into the hold and 'swore blind that he had seen a rat'. It was decided to try to flush the rat out, so the pond-boards and everything else that was in the hold was brought on deck, the engine started and the hose switched on. No sign of the rat. No sign at all. There were two men down in the hold, big Billy McCrindle from Girvan with a deck-broom and Johnny Gibson with the hose. Suddenly the rat was sighted, emerging from beneath the bilge-stringer. 'There it is! There it is!' some of the crew on deck began shouting.

So there was Johnny Gibson running about in the hold with the hose and big Billy trying to get the rat with the brush and, the next thing, the end of the hose was down in Billy's boot and the boot was filling with water and him shouting,'Waatch hoot ye're daein!' By this time there was quite an audience, other crews having come aboard to see what was going on. Anyway, the unlucky rat was eventually killed and the crew started to put the stuff back below, but what happened next? Another rat appeared from beneath the bilge-stringer! [Matt Sloan]

One year the Ayrshire boats were left in the Crinan Canal over Christmas, and when the crews came back they found the boats frozen in. Through the night somebody woke up hearing a SQUEAK SQUEAK SQUEAK SQUEAK. He gave his shipmates a shake and they all went up on deck. There were hundreds of rats on the ice, attracted by old food that had been thrown out of the boats. That was the only time that Angus McCrindle saw a rat on board a boat. When the crew went to lay the net aft, they discovered him and then trapped him between a couple of frames, where he was killed with a brush-handle. [Angus McCrindle]

Scarts

Shooting a ring-net in the Sound of Hellisay one night, when the search-light was switched on, scarts (cormorants, shags) 'came off the cliff like bullets'. When the crew began to haul the net, the wide wings were covered in enmeshed birds. The clearing of the net took hours and many of the birds were dead. The cliffs being nesting-place of scarts, that phenomenon recurred every night a crew shot there. [Iain Gemmell]

Playing a trick on Dick Andrew

Andy McCrindle recalled a similar experience one night when a netful of herring was rung against the rocks on the north side of the Sound of Hellisay. Startled by the lights, scarts were diving off the rocks and striking the boats, and half-a-dozen of these birds were caught and confined in the wheelhouse of the *Maireared*. When the skipper, Dick Andrew, went to enter the wheelhouse, after the herring had been taken aboard, 'he wis met by a whole dose o angry scarts!' [Andy McCrindle]

'Flying bombs'

When Duncan 'Porter' Gillies of the *Mallaig Mhor* rung one night close to Muldonich, the boats – *Lady of Fatima* was his neighbour – were 'bombarded with cormorants'. The searchlights that the crews were employing, to start the herring off the shore and into the net, 'put paid to their sleep on the cliffs. We had to duck, take cover, till the cormorants stopped coming. The searchlight blinded them and woe betide you if you got hit.' The birds – which Duncan MacInnes described as 'flying bombs' – knocked off the stove-pipe and a side-light.

On another occasion, at the Weaver's Castle, John MacInnes – an old fishermen who had once worked at drift-nets, skippering the *St Columba* – was hit on the chest by a cormorant and 'bowled right over'. The Eriskay men used to go in along cliffs where cormorants roosted and by shouting or shining the searchlight would get a few fatalities for the pot. 'They were great for soup,' Duncan MacInnes recalled, but they could also be boiled, with a whole onion inside each one, and 'tasted as good as the best beef joint'. 'Black' Jim Manson of Mallaig called the scart 'the Eriskay turkey'. [Duncan MacInnes]

Waterfalls

Once, in a gale of south-west wind, going up the Sound of Mull, along the Morvern shore, where burns run over the cliff-edge in waterfalls, the wind was so strong that these burns were being turned at the top and their spray 'blown all over the place'. The crew counted 26 such sights that day. [Iain Gemmell]

Gossamer

It was a beautiful sunny day in Loch Boisdale, but in dead of winter. Gossamer threads were blowing in the light air. 'A lovely day this, Bob,' Archie Graham remarked to Bob Morans, who steered his boat, the *Margaret Rose*. 'Dae ye think so?' Bob replied, and Archie knew at once that he'd said something wrong. 'What made you say that, Bob?' he asked. 'Well,' Bob said, 'back winds after frost, stand by for a hard blow.' Bob was right. It blew a hard gale that day, and he had seen the signs – frost earlier on and a change in wind direction to a southerly, warmer air.

Many years later, Archie was sitting at home in Peninver – a coastal village, five miles north of Campbeltown – watching television. The weatherman, Jack Scott, was giving his forecast, and the chart for that day showed wind from northward and temperatures well below freezing. 'Tomorrow will be a nice day,' he said, indicating an arrow from a southerly direction and the temperature well above freezing. 'Old Bob wouldn't have agreed with Jack Scott today,' Archie remarked to his wife. Scott appeared on television the next day and apologised for having been so far out in the previous day's forecast. The gale had come. [Archie Graham]

Wartime
. . . .

On 4 May 1942, a Sunderland of 228 Squadron left Oban to ferry two Naval officers to South Uist. On their first approach, the pilots judged that there was insufficient room to land, went round again and touched down, but the starboard float struck a submerged rock and the pilots decided to take off. While executing a climbing turn to avoid cliffs, the aircraft stalled and hit a small island and settled in 12 to 15ft of water. The fore end of the aircraft was very badly damaged and her back broken, though the rear section remained above water. The badly-injured crew was taken ashore and cared for by nuns until transferred to hospital in Oban, where both pilots died.[9]

At the time of the accident, there were two boats lying at Lochboisdale quay, the *Lily* of Campbeltown and the *Fionnaghal* of Tarbert, partners at the ring-net. These boats were called out and took crew and passengers off the wrecked aircraft. Archibald Stewart, who skippered the *Lily*, recalled – accurately or otherwise – that the boats 'took thirty off her'. Both skippers were asked to 'stand by', and remained in attendance at Lochboisdale for two days, in case their services were further required. They were recompensed for the two days' fishing they lost, having claimed for an average of the daily landings at Mallaig – there was 'good money' going at the time – and received £250 per boat. Both 'Baldy' Stewart and the *Fionnaghal*'s skipper, Donald McDougall, were awarded the British Empire Medal for their services. [Archibald Stewart]

A mine at Canna

The *Bluebird* and her neighbour, the *Enterprise*, were at Canna. It was a gannet fishing and they were doing well, not least with catches of mackerel. The *Bluebird* shot on a diving gannet this particular day – a Thursday – and, when they 'met the boats', Alex Black, Danny McLean and Sandy McKinlay jumped aboard from the neighbour-boat to assist with hauling the net. The first thing Sandy McKinlay – 'Dory' as he was nick-named

– said when he jumped aboard was: 'That's a wile sight o mines that's up in Stag Bey there. There's three or fower mines up in that bey.' Duncan Blair was hauling the foot-rope on the fore barrel of the winch and, with only two or three stops aboard, the rope tightened and wouldn't come any more: the net was 'fast'. Now, this was happening on a part of the coast that the fishermen were 'dead sure' held no rocks or wrecks that would snag a net. 'This net's fast!' Duncan exclaimed. 'Aw for God's seck,' the skipper, Charlie Durnin, protested, 'did ye ever see a net fast here in yer life?' – 'Never mind whoot we saw, Cherlie – this net's fast,' Duncan replied, looking over the side of the boat. Then, to Alex 'Roarin' Black: 'Here, haev a look at that doon there an see if you ever saw anythin laik it while you were in the Navy.' Alec looked, and there it was – a big mine. So the crew shouted across to the neighbour-boat, which was linked by a tow-rope to the *Bluebird*'s starboard side, 'We're fast on a mine!' As soon as the neighbouring skipper, Willie 'Toon' MacDonald, heard that, he threw his sweepline over the side and was off! As luck had it, with the weight of the mine the net parted from back to sole, and the mine sunk away. After that excitement, the fishermen decided they had enough of Canna. 'If there's mines on this coast o Canna,' one of them reasoned, 'it's time we wir gettin out of it,' so they shifted out to the Heisgeir. That was in August 1945, 'the year,' as Duncan Blair recalled, 'that 'Toon' cam oot fae Canna and told us aboot this terrible bomb that wis dropped on Japan.' [Duncan Blair]

'Underground pork'

Some 26 years after the above story was recorded, Duncan Campbell – who was 'boy' aboard the Enterprise *– was able to add both a prologue and a sequel to the narrative. 'Underground pork' was one of the expressions – 'bunnies' was another – that fishermen used to avoid saying the tabboo word, 'rabbit'.*

The *Bluebird* and *Enterprise* went alongside a puffer that was lying in Canna harbour and the crews were offered some of the rabbits that the puffer's skipper had shot on the island. The *Enterprise*'s skipper, 'Toon', was so superstitious that he wouldn't even take aboard any salmon that happened to be caught during fishing operations, and he vehemently refused the offer of the rabbits when it was relayed to him by Duncan Campbell. The *Bluebird*'s crew had no such qualms, and tucked into half-a-rabbit each for dinner, while 'Toon's' men had to make do with corned beef with their potatoes and cabbage.

That same day, a shepherd on the island reported to the fishermen: 'Right between the Stac an the Lion, there a mine. Ye'll see it at low water, but ye'll no see it at high water – its wire must be stuck in a rock.' Notwithstanding that warning, the *Bluebird* rang there (Duncan remembers that a surface rush of mackerel tempted 'Duke' Durnin).

The damaged net took two weeks of intermittent mending to repair, and, seeing the *Bluebird's* crew thus engaged, 'Toon' would taunt them gleefully: 'There ye are – that's yer underground fuckin pork for ye now!' [Duncan Campbell]

An invitation to Dunvegan Castle

Three pairs of Campbeltown boats were lying in Dunvegan harbour one week-end in 1944. On Sunday morning, a big Rolls Royce drove down the pier. This was Dame Flora Macleod, and she invited all the fishermen up to her residence, Dunvegan Castle. Some of them accepted the offer and walked the half-mile or so to the castle, to be received there by Dame Flora, who explained, before showing the men around the castle, that she wanted to do something for them, since the war was still on and they were performing a vital service supplying food to the nation. [Francis McWhirter]

A butter bonanza

A cargo was being discharged from a MacBrayne steamer in Lochboisdale when a crate fell into the water. It floated up and some fishermen caught hold of it and dumped it in the engine-room of one of the boats. A search was made for the crate, but no one came aboard the fishing-boat to look, and the crate was never found. It contained 56lbs of butter, which was duly 'dished out among the fleet'. At that time, the crews were on civilian rations, so the butter was a welcome addition to an otherwise sparse diet. Later, fishermen were allowed the more generous seamen's ration, which put them in 'great order'. [Denis Meenan]

The Gestapo

During the Second World War, Grieve Gemmell of Dunure, in common with many fishermen, ceased to be a fisherman and instead became a recruit in the Royal Navy. He was sent to St Luke's, the engineers' training school in Lowestoft. At times the tedium of life there, as a second class stoker, irked him, therefore he was intrigued by the ease with which fellow-sailors were waved through the gate by the simple expedient of holding up a sheet of paper to the guard. He decided to try it, so he got a sheet of paper, ran towards the gate and was told: 'Carry on.'

When he returned, however, from his illicit spell of freedom, the guard was rather less accommodating and he was stopped. 'Here! What are you doing? When did you become a messenger?' he was asked. 'A'm no a messenger,' he replied. 'A wis watchin they boys runnin oot an A thought that wis what ye did when ye went oot.' At that point a man appeared, wearing a petty officer's uniform. 'Aha!' he exclaimed. 'It's you, Grieve.' This was Peter McDougall of Tarbert, one of the 'Toms'. 'Aye, it's me,' Grieve replied. 'Ye'll be all right,' Peter assured him. 'A'm with the Gestapo here.' The 'Gestapo' was the popular nick-name for the guards, and Grieve got off with his exploit. [Grieve Gemmell]

VE Day

Francis McWhirter was with Jock Meenan in the *Gratitude* when World War II officially ended on 8 May 1945. The boat was lying in Mallaig when they heard the news and they went straight home to Campbeltown around the Mull of Kintyre. Night had fallen by the time they entered the Firth of Clyde, and bonfires could be seen burning all along the Ayrshire coast in celebration of Victory in Europe Day. One of Francis's shipmates, Denis Meenan – who was Jock Meenan's nephew – had even greater reason to remember that day, because when he arrived home his call-up papers were waiting for him and he went away to the Navy. [Francis McWhirter]

Showers

One day, when some of the Campbeltown ringers were lying in Lochboisdale, the commander of the RAF base there came down and asked if there were any herring to be had. He was given an abundance of fish, much to his delight. While he was chatting with the fishermen, he happened to ask where they bathed, and was promptly shown the fish-hold and a basin there – one foot in the basin of water, wash one side of the body, then the other foot in the basin and wash the other side. 'Right,' he announced, 'Saturday afternoon, no RAF bathing – fishermen only.' The older fishermen refused go to the showers at the base, but those who did avail themselves of the facilities emerged feeling 'top o the pops'.

Dirty clothes were parcelled up and posted home. When the return parcel arrived, containing the clean clothing, the fishermen always hoped for 'wee tit-bits' within. The only article of clothing not sent home was dungarees, which would be towed astern on passage to Mallaig, and hung on deck to dry on the passage back, if the day was fine. [Duncan Campbell]

Yarns

········

Many of the stories in this book qualify as 'yarns', but those that follow are grouped under that heading because they do not fit comfortably into any of the other chapters. A 'yarn', by my definition, is just the same as a story, but it's a story that can last, that may be told and retold and cease to be the property of an individual or crew or even community. There is no copyright on oral tradition: yarns and wisecracks circulate and mutate until, ultimately, the 'classics' of the genre gain a life-force independent of the individuals whose wit and invention brought them into being. Boats' forecastles and the street-corners and net-stores, where fishermen gathered when ashore, were the main places yarns were traded; but the atmosphere of these gatherings, sadly, could never be reproduced in a mere book.

The ring-net, in Hugh Edgar's opinion, was 'more sociable' than any of the jobs – seine-netting, mid-water trawling and pelagic trawling – which succeeded it, because, in the Minch and elsewhere, crews lay alongside crews from other ports and there was a chance to talk. 'There wis never another job quite like the ring-net for excitement an time off when ye wir a young fella,' he reflected. Subsequent jobs were more solitary and intensive and 'people wirna faces – they wir voices on the wireless, because the social thing went oot it at the end o the ring-net, a big lot o it anyway'.

Sociability naturally engendered good relations among fishermen from different ports. 'There wis a wee bit o harmony then,' Ian Gibson recalled. Once, when the Britannia's *net was 'knocked in bits', no fewer than 60 fishermen – from Kintyre as well as Ayrshire – assembled on Lochboisdale Pier to mend it.*

Stars and stripes

One summer in the North, the McDougalls of Tarbert ventured round the west side of Barra, into the open Atlantic. After a while, an old fellow, Alec Johnstone, who was aboard the *Mairearad*, called to the skipper,

Archie 'Tom': 'It's time ye wir turnin, Erchie.' – 'How?' queried Archie. The old fellow's answer was: 'There's a gannet passed there wi stars an stripes on its wings!' [Robert Ross]

The blessing of the *Village Belle III*

The MacKinnon brothers in Eriskay bought a boat from Tarbert, Harris. She was a sister ship of the Jacksons' *Village Belle III*, of Tarbert, Loch Fyne, therefore as like her as could be. The *Village Belle* was lying at the pier in Lochboisdale just days after the MacKinnons had bought their boat and Neil Jackson and his crew were asleep below. Neil awoke hearing walking on the deck and got up to see what was going on. When he stuck his head out of the scuttle he was surprised to see Catholic priests performing a ceremony of blessing. They had mistaken his boat for the MacKinnons' new acquisition, assisted in their error by the name 'Tarbert' painted on the *Belle*'s stern. Though not himself a Catholic, Neil let the ceremony proceed, explaining: 'Mind ye, it dinna bother me that much … A wis kinna superstitious too. It would've been worse if they'd stopped. Imagine me runnin aboot wi a boat that wis only half-blessed!' [Neil Jackson]

An imagined otter

The *Harvest Queen* of Carradale was lying in Loch Skiport one night in the early 1950s and no one would leave the forecastle because there was a noise coming from the deck and somebody mentioned 'otter'. The irrational fear of this otter, that lay in wait in the outer darkness, gathered such momentum – with warnings like, 'A winna go up there – it'll catch ye by the leg' – that the crew 'winna even go up for a pee, anybody!' The noise that had so unnerved everyone turned out to be a tarpaulin flapping in the wind. [Neil McDougall]

The lobster-creel

A few of the ring-net fishermen carried a creel or two with them in the Minch and, as a diversion, would bait and sink the pots in the hope of catching a lobster. One day, Matt Sloan went into Billy's Bight, at the south end of Loch Eynort, and away up in the wee creek at the head of the bight there was evidence of a creel, in the form of a bunch of corks – the marker. So, he nosed the *Watchful* in and in until the creel-rope could be caught and the creel – which was empty – hauled aboard.

'This'll be Angus's creel,' somebody remarked. Angus was Angus McCrindle, another Maidens skipper, and a brother-in-law of Matt Sloan's. Andy Alexander, one of the crew, stuffed a couple of lemonade bottles and an old cut-up seaboot into the creel, which was then returned to the seabed. Not a word was said about this, outwith the crew, until one day they heard a Campbeltown skipper, Pat McKay, talking on the radio to somebody about the creel he had up in Loch Eynort. 'A don't know who did it,' he said, 'but somebody … A picked up a creel an it was full o leemonade bottles an old seaboots.' Next time the *Watchful* was alongside the *Regina Maris*, the Ayrshiremen owned up to Pat: 'We wir the culprits.' [Matt Sloan]

Cousin Rodney's first-born

The Ayrshire ringers, the *Elizmor*, the *May Queen* and the first *Wistaria*, had lain in Loch Skiport for three days, in February 1951. Their respective neighbours were on the other side of the Minch, in Mallaig. It was towards the end of the fishing season, there wasn't a lot doing and the weather was broken. Contact had been made with the crews in Mallaig, whose feeling was that it was time to quit and return to the Clyde, and there was agreement on that. It wasn't a pleasant night – the wind was in on the shore – when the three boats left Skiport and steamed south and into Lochboisdale.

When they had moored there, one of the *Wistaria*'s crew went up to the telephone-box and rang home. Rodney Sloan – a crew-member and cousin of the skipper, Matt Sloan – had been married relatively recently, and when his shipmate returned from 'phoning, he announced that Rodney's wife Grace had had a son, the couple's first child, on 31 January.

The crew at once insisted that, in the circumstances, Rodney could do nothing else but take them up to the hotel for a meal that night. 'Will A really need tae?' Rodney asked, rather dubiously. 'Oh,' said Matt, 'A think ye'll need tae. A think it's definitely necessary'. Another cousin, Eddie McEwan, who skippered the *Elizmor*, heard of the proposal and also approached Rodney. 'A'm a cousin o yours, as well,' he argued. 'What aboot me?' Following that encounter, Rodney returned to Matt and said: 'Look, what about it? Have A got tae take them as well?' Matt dismissed this new, mischievous development: 'Ye don't bother. They're no your crew. Jeest oorsels.' So, Rodney set off for the hotel and arranged the meal.

At the agreed time, off went the crew to the hotel and were treated to nothing more elaborate than a cup of tea and a boiled egg! That – a belated high tea – was all that was on offer; and before the crew left, each of them signed an entry – marking the occasion of the celebration of Rodney's first-born child – in the hotel visitors' book. [Matt Sloan]

In Dunvegan Castle

The fleet was at Dunvegan and some of the Ayrshire fishermen took a notion to see through Dunvegan Castle. A lady there, who appeared to be caretaker, agreed to conduct them on a tour. In one room, they were shown the famous silken Fairy Flag, which is believed to have magical powers, and which Matt Sloan remembered as 'only a remnant of a flag – it wis tattered an torn and disintegrating with age; but there it was'. There were other less revered relics in the room, including an old blunderbuss in a glass case. On the subject of the blunderbuss, the lady had an anecdote to relate. 'English as I am,' she began, 'I did have one day a party of English visitors here …' The fishermen at this stage got the distinct impression that their guide was becoming weary of the banal questions such visitors invariably put to her. Anyway, when that particular party caught sight of the blunderbuss, one of them exclaimed, 'Oh, goodness, and what is that?' to which her reply was: 'Oh, the MacLeods used that for shooting midges on the top of MacLeod's Tables'* [Matt Sloan]

The Morris Cowley

All accounts of this incident vary substantially. I have chosen this version because the informant skippered the boat that was damaged and was actually there at the time.

This infamous incident of c. 1935 took place at Lochboisdale on a Saturday morning, when a high-spirited group of Campbeltown fishermen commandeered a Morris Cowley van belonging to an islander. One Campbeltown skipper, who was old enough to have known better, was 'as bad as any boy', climbing in and out the vehicle, shouting, 'Come on – Daliburgh! This way for Daliburgh!' In the end, the van went over the quay with 'Tit' Ralston inside it. It landed, nose-first, on the fore-

*The two flat hills that rise above Loch Bracadale.

deck of the *King Fisher*, breaking three carlins and six feet of planking next to the scuttle. The weight of the van then pushed the boat out from the quay, and the van itself toppled into the water. 'Tit' was still inside the van, struggling to escape. Finally, he managed to burst the door open and climb out just as the van was submerging.

This fiasco caused a sensation on the quay, and some of the more serious-minded skippers – Dan Conley and Duncan Graham among them – threw off their ropes and retreated to an anchor. In the clear water, the van could be seen, and a team of fishermen set to work to salvage it. A huge bowline was tied on the end of a rope, and the loop dropped over the van. Next, the men got poles and turned the van on to its wheels. 'Baldy' Stewart's *King Bird* was on the beach up ahead, having her bottom coated with anti-fouling paint. When the tide had risen to the level of her engine's water-pump, the engine was started and the van winched on to the beach on the end of the rope. The little bull-nosed Morris was left lying there until the tide ebbed further, when a group of fishermen – Jock McIntyre, Baldy Stewart, Willie Stewart, 'Mecky' Wilkinson, James 'Gypsy' Robertson, 'Tit' and Ian Mitchell – got round it and pushed it on to the road and then along to the quay.

The sump was drained and the magneto and plugs removed and dried on top of a stove. Once these parts had been cleaned and restored to the engine, lubricating-oil added, and a gallon of petrol put in the tank, the engine was switched on … and it went! By this time, the fishermen, having feared the worst, had parted with £15 to the van's owner, in compensation; and he had gone and bought another old Morris Cowley from MacKenzie's Hotel. Undoubtedly, he got the best of the deal! [John McIntyre]

Angus Edward MacInnes, in his Eriskay Where I Was Born *(p 120), describes the vehicle as a butcher's van belonging to a worthy, Angus MacLellan.*

A youthful-looking skipper

The *Harvest Queen* of Carradale was lying in Mallaig one week-end, and on the Saturday her skipper Archie Paterson – then a man of 25 years – got busy repairing a net. Turner McCrindle, an older Maidens fisherman, spied Archie with needle and twine and approached him to offer words of encouragement. 'That's right, son,' he said, 'learn young, learn fair.' He thought Archie was the boat's boy! [Archibald Paterson]

The Haircut

The *Harvest Queen* of Carradale was returning home from a trip to the North and 'the trim was good' among her crew. Archie Paterson, the skipper, remarked to one of his crew, 'Fergie' Paterson, a cousin: 'A'll need tae get ma hair cut – it's very long.' – 'Oh,' Fergie said, 'A know the very man'll do it for ye.' Fergie's name was actually Donald, but his mother was a Ferguson from Loch Maddy, so he got 'Fergie' after her. 'He was the best I've known for seein herrin in the water,' Archie recollected. 'Ye could depend on him. And he was full of fun at the same time.'

While the boat was at a certain port on her passage home, Archie, furnished with directions from 'Fergie', went ashore to find the hairdresser, and found him, an elderly man, alone with his wife in a harbourside tenement. 'Aye, A'll cut yer hair,' said the man. 'Well,' Archie insisted, 'don't take too much off – just a trim.' As Archie soon found out, 'if ye asked him tae do a thing, he'd do the very opposite'. 'Fergie' already knew this and when Archie made his way back to the boat, sporting a 'rumper' – his locks shorn 'intae the wood' – his cousin was waiting for him, 'bent double laughin'. Archie knew that his wife wouldn't be amused when she saw the haircut he had, and 'Fergie' knew that too.

It was only then that 'Fergie' revealed a story about the hairdresser. He'd had a shop and quarrelled severely with one of his customers, but the man eventually returned one day and sat for a shave. The hairdresser placed an open razor in a mug of boiling water while he soaped the face of his returned customer, and, when he had him ready to shave, caught him by the nose and said to him: 'A've got ye now, ye so-and-so.' With that, he took the razor and drew the blunt end of it across the man's throat. Feeling the hot edge, the man thought his throat was slit and that the warm water running down his neck was blood. In a panic, he rose out of the chair and ran into the street shouting that his throat had been cut. The hairdresser's business thereafter declined and he apparently lost his shop. [Archie Paterson]

The End
· · · · · · · · · · ·

The decline of ring-netting effectively began between the Wars when seine-netting for white fish and dredging for scallops were introduced to the Clyde, offering remunerative alternatives to ring-netting and off-season long-lining. At first, these methods were employed only when herring-fishing was slack, but, increasingly, numbers of crews began to devote a greater part of their working year to white fish and clams and ultimately, in the post-war period, there were those who specialised and completely abandoned herring-fishing.

When the market for Nephrops Norvegicus – or 'prawns' – expanded in the late 1950s, even more herring-fishermen switched to prawn-trawling, first as a seasonal job and finally as virtually an all-year-round job. Ring-netting, by the 1960s, was therefore pursued only by the most committed of crews, many of whom, never the less, were forced to diversify when the herring fishing slackened or failed.

The adoption of the Scandinavian purse seine-net – a close relative of the ring-net – by fishermen on the East Coast of Scotland from 1966 onwards, and of the mid-water trawl generally, in the same period, brought into herring-fishing two new and phenomenally productive methods. For the Clyde herring-fishermen, mid-water-trawls were initially carried only to complement the ring-net, but finally, in the early 1970s, the ring-net was entirely abandoned and trawls alone used. The Carradale fishermen were the most vociferous in their opposition to mid-water trawling and demanded its prohibition from Clyde waters, but in the end they too succumbed to the inevitable.

Mid-water trawling

In the late 1960s and early 1970s, a new fishery for hake, using mid-water pair-trawls, was opened up in the deep water off the north end of Arran. This form of herring-trawling was experimented with in the North, on nights when the ring-net was unsuitable for herring-fishing, but without much success initially, because the fishermen's 'hearts weren't in it'. As the 1970s progressed, however, more and more success was made of the job, both for white fish and herring. But the fishing fleet was changing and by the end of the 1970s, 'most of the well-known names had disappeared' and the Maidens and Girvan fleets had dwindled. [Iain Gemmell]

Angus McCrindle gave up ring-netting in 1972. The family boats weren't in the Minch after that year. Podlies, hake and dogfish in the Clyde kept them going. Even in 1971, Angus in the *Investors* and his son Angus in the old *Saffron* had ring-nets as well as mid-water trawls in the North. One night they got 210 cran of herring with the mid-water trawl off the Curachan Bank. They left there in northerly wind and, during the passage to Mallaig, the end of the ring-net on the *Investors*' stern, though tied down, was washed overboard and pulled the net from below the tyings. All that remained, by the time Angus was alerted to the calamity, was the sole-rope. The crew got that aboard, then both boats steamed straight up through the wind with searchlights probing, saw one of the net-buoys and got the net – which, being sole-less, was all afloat – back aboard. 'We wir three days pittin that ring-net thegither,' Angus recalled. 'But we shouldnae've hid the ring-net on the boat in the first place, because we wir up tae dae mid-watter trawlin, but we wir jeest at that stage: Will we get them wi the ring-net? Will we get them wi the trawl?' [Angus McCrindle]

During the last couple of years that Jim Munro spent in the North with the *Britannia*, a mid-water trawl was carried aboard, but the ring-net remained first choice – 'A don't think there's ever been a job quite like it', he remarked with unconcealed nostalgia. On nights when the moon was full and bright and tides were strong, however, the crews went 'over tae the Tiree side' and trawled in Gott Bay and Hynish Bay with some success, though, in these pre-net-monitor years, tearings were more frequent and days would be spent ashore mending trawls. He attributed the demise of ring-netting to the pursers' catching herring in deep water before the shoals could reach the shallow, and to their ability to supply the markets with greater bulk. [Jim Munro]

Purse-seining

Grieve Gemmell remembered big purse-seiners shooting their nets off Skye and going away to market 'doon by the heid wi herrin'. Next night they were back out and he overheard one skipper say to another on the radio: 'There no much tae be seen the night.' The other skipper agreed, adding: 'Ye wonder where they go tae.' Grieve felt like butting into the discussion and pointing out: 'Ye've jeest ta'en them all awa!' [Grieve Gemmell]

Last in the North

The *Stella Maris* and *Fiona*, skippered by the Meenan brothers, Jim and Denis, were probably the last pair of Campbeltown ring-netters in the Minch, and 1967 was their last year there. In that year, too, James Macdonald of Campbeltown, in the *Regina Maris*, was in the North neighbouring Alec 'Sugar' McCrindle's *Heritage* (ex-*Minicoy*) of Maidens. The Meenans had bought the *Fiona* in 1963 and worked her, in partnership with the *Stella*, for four years in the North. They fished exceptionally well during these four years and paid her off in the first year. 'Oh, jeest fell intae it,' Denis Meenan recalled. 'We jeest twigged the thing in the Minch. Every night we got herrin. That's when we started realisin how tae fish the ring-net.' But by then the ring-net fishery was almost over.

The wrong job

When Neil Jackson started working among the bigger purse-seiners, especially on Coll Bank, the purser-skippers told him on the radio that he was at the wrong job. 'This is your job, really,' they said. They also told him that he and his brother wouldn't catch any herring: 'We're seein them on the sonar – they're goin too fast for yer ring-net.' By this time, the Jacksons carried both a ring-net and a mid-water trawl on the stern, so they 'whipped oot the trawls efter that'. That night they had 280 cran with the trawl.

On his last trip North, in the mid-1970s, Neil Jackson had no ring-net at all with him but was mid-water pair-trawling with his brother. They shot in Corodale and took 220 units – the new measurement of 100 kilos, crans having been discontinued – which he took aboard his own boat and ran to market. The price per unit was £40 and for that single tow, of about 20 minutes' duration, the two crews earned £350 a man. On his way to market, he spoke on the radio to the Eriskay skipper, Calum MacKinnon, who asked him: 'How did you get on there?' Neil replied: 'Oh, a hunder cran anyway.' – 'That's a big shot just now, with the prices that's in it,' Calum replied, adding: 'That's the first herrin that's been in there this winter. They must've been waitin on you comin.' This was after New Year. The Clyde was closed to herring-fishing at that time and the Jacksons were determined not to go to prawn-trawling, so when they returned home it was to mid-water trawling for white fish they went. [Neil Jackson]

As ring-netting entered its decline in the 1960s, attitudes within the fishing communities began to change. Crews were less willing to spend lengthy periods away from home. Grieve Gemmell, for example, did a six-week trip around the time he got engaged in 1948; in later years, it became the norm to spend two weeks away and come home on the third week-end; latterly, Grieve said, crews wanted to come home every week-end. 'It wis purgatory up and doon that road,' he said. 'That spiled the North fishin, hame every week.' His old fishing-partner, Willie Anderson agreed. Four or five weeks was the normal duration of a trip North in the early years, and then 'it wis doon tae aboot a fortnight at last'. The boats took 'some awfu batterins' crossing the Minch to get to Crinan, and the crews had some 'some terrible journeys' by road to reach home; yet, they were there for only a night and day, and away back North again.

Attitudes ashore were changing too. Fishermen increasingly wanted a regular income, and when car-ownership, for example, became general, crews needed money every week to run the cars. The three or four month summer slack in the herring fishing was no longer tolerable. Younger wives too preferred to have money in their hand every week. [Peter McDougall, Robert Ross]

By the mid-1970s, ring-netting had become history, not just in the North, where the method attained its greatest ever productivity, but everywhere.

APPENDIX 1
BIOGRAPHICAL NOTES ON MAIN CONTRIBUTORS

Years in brackets following each entry refer to when the information was recorded or submitted. Contributors who had died by the time the book was completed are denoted with an asterisk.

Andy Alexander*, b 1928, Maidens. His mother's family, the Andrews, were notable fishermen. Fished with Matt Sloan, first on the *Bairn's Pride* for about two years, then on the *Watchful*, from her arrival in Maidens in 1959 until her departure in 1972. Subsequently had the *Freedom* with Hugh McPhee, then his own boats, the *Argosy* followed by the *Elizmor*. After leaving the sea, was harbourmaster at Maidens and port officer at Ayr. [1976]

Willie Anderson, b 1922, Dunure. Went to fishing first in 1936 in the *Bonito*, part-owned by his father. In 1948, after naval service, bought the *Erica*; in 1959 had the *Jasmine* built. His final boat, before retirement, was the *Prospector*. Was Chairman of the Clyde Fishermen's Association and Scottish Fishermen's Organisation and was awarded an MBE. [1999]

Duncan Blair*, b 1902, Campbeltown, son of Dugald Blair. Went to fishing in January 1917. Crewed the Blair family boats *Glad Tidings* and *Bengullion*, the latter built by Reekie, St Monans, in 1928. Was then on Charlie Durnin's *Bluebird*; thereafter Hector Gilchrist's *Maureen*. [1974]

Joe Brown, b 1936, Campbeltown. First berth was with Tommy Ralston in the *Golden Fleece*, followed by a spell in the Durnins' *Bluebird*. Joined the Meenans' *Stella Maris* when 18 years old and remained there for 13 years. Retired in 1993 as skipper of the prawn-trawler *True Token*. Has since built many model boats. [1998]

Duncan Campbell, born 1926, Campbeltown. His first berth was aboard Archie Cook's *Enterprise*, skippered by Willie 'Toon' MacDonald. Subsequently owned the *Quiet Waters* and *Eliezer* with Alex McGeachy. His last berth was in Jim Speed's *Speedwell*, from which he retired c 1990. Popularly known as 'Kemmel' (his own preferred spelling), a corrupt form of *Caimbeul*, which is Gaelic for Campbell. [2000]

Hugh Edgar, b 1940, Dunure. He joined his father, John 'Jonah' Edgar, on the *Hercules*, in July 1955, and, owing to his father's deteriorating health, began skippering the boat at the early age of 19. By May 1963, he had assumed full command. His last winter of ring-netting in the North was in 1967. He owned two subsequent vessels – also named *Hercules* – before retiring from fishing in January 1996, and now lives in Ayr and works as second mate on a Stand By Vessel in the North Sea oil industry. [2000]

Cecil Finn, b 1936, Campbeltown. Was in North for seven years with the *Stella Maris*, then turned to seine-netting. Owned and part-owned a succession of seine-net boats, beginning with the *Gleaner*. His prominent role in national fisheries politics, as Vice-President and then President of the Scottish Fishermen's Federation, earned him an MBE and OBE. [1998]

Iain Gemmell, b 1934, Dunure, son of John Gemmell. He went to sea in the summer of 1949 aboard the *Summer Rose* with his father and Uncle Willie. In 1957 he had a spell on the Andersons' *Marie*, followed by a spell with the Munros on the *New Dawn*. In 1962, he and his cousin Grieve formed a partnership and had the *Storm Drift III* built by Noble of Girvan. He sold up and came ashore in 1992. [1999, 2000]

Grieve Gemmell, b 1925, Dunure, son of Sammy Gemmell. His first berth was in *Storm Drift I*, in 1939. In 1943 went into Royal Navy. Took command of *Storm Drift II* in 1960, then *Storm Drift III* in 1962. Neighboured Willie Anderson for many years. Retired through ill health in 1988. [1999, 2000]

Ian Gibson, b 1929, Dunure, and still living there. Went to the fishing, aged 14, in the *Britannia* (BA 130), owned by his father Tommy and uncle Sandy. His first command was in 1958, of a later *Britannia*, built in 1955. Owned and skippered a succession of boats, ending with the *Gratitude*, from which he retired in 1999. [2000]

Archie Graham, b 1923, Peninver, Kintyre. Began fishing, aged 16, aboard his father Duncan Graham's *Falcon*. Went to War in 1942 and in 1947 took delivery of the new boat, *Margaret Rose*, which his father hadn't lived to see. Sold her in 1958 and has since worked with smaller boats at salmon nets, lobster creels, etc. [1999]

Neil Jackson, b 1926, Tarbert. His first berth, in 1940, was on the *Village Belle II*, which he subsequently commanded. Skippered the two subsequent *Village Belles*, always in partnership with his brother Willie ('The Count'). Retired c 1985. [1998, 1999, 2000]

Duncan McArthur, b 1925, Campbeltown. His first berth was in the *Crimson Arrow*, skippered by his maternal grandfather, James McLean. Was subsequently on the *Bluebird*, *Shenandoah*, *Glen Carradale* and *Amalthea*. In 1951, the family ringer, the *Mary McLean* was launched, and Duncan remained with her until his retirement, having in 1966 given up ring-netting for prawn-trawling. [2000]

James McCreath*, b 1897, Girvan. Notable ring-net skipper. Fished the *Aurora* and then the *May* in partnership with his brother Jock of the *A J J & T*. Was known as 'Kruger'. [1976]

Andy McCrindle, b 1924, Maidens, but lives in Barassie, Troon. His first berth was in 1940 in the family-owned *Golden Sheaf*. In 1959 took command of the *Silver Fern* and, after she was sold in 1966, emigrated to New Zealand. He returned to Scotland in 1974 and had a further spell at sea with Sandy Munro in the *Fair Morn* before coming ashore to work. He retired in 1989. His nick-name, 'Professor' – from his academic success in school – distinguished him from his McCrindle namesake in Girvan, Andy 'Tarry'. [2000]

T Angus McCrindle, b 1924, Maidens. His first full command was the *Minicoy*, c. 1952; then skippered the new *Sapphire*. In 1970, he had the *Investors* built. Finally, in 1973, a second *Saffron* was built. He has, for many years, been interested in photography and has also built four models of the *Saffron*. [1999]

J Turner McCrindle*, b 1902, Maidens. A brother of Angus above and an estimable tradition-bearer. Went to drift-nets aboard the *Eagle*, on holidays from school. He spent his working life aboard family boats, starting in 1916 on the nabby *Silver Spray*, followed by the three named *Margarita*, then the *Saffron*, and finally the *Sapphire*. He wrote prolifically after his retirement, chiefly religious verse. Published a booklet, *Poems by a Fisherman*. [1976]

James Macdonald, b 1925, Campbeltown. His first berth was aboard the *Amber Queen* of Rothesay. He skippered first the *Harvest Hope* and then the *Regina Maris*. In 1970 had the steel trawler *Crimson Arrow* built at Campbeltown and thereafter owned a string of fishing vessels, ending with the *Village Maid*, from which he retired in 1988. [2000]

Neil McDougall, b 1940, Carradale. Son of Matthew McDougall and better known by his nick-name, 'Donna'. Went to the fishing when he left school and was about three years with Archie Paterson on the *Harvest Queen*, before going ashore to work as a carpenter. Is a fund of knowledge concerning the histories of fishing boats. [2000]

Peter McDougall, b 1941, Tarbert. His first berth was with his uncle Archie on the *Mairearad*. Had a year at seine-netting with the *Nancy Glen* to broaden his experience and then skippered the *Fionnaghal*. Fished in New Zealand and Australia before returning to Tarbert and successive ownership of two boats by name of *Silver Spray*. Retired in 1995. [2000]

Hugh MacFarlane*, b 1884, Tarbert. A marvellous tradition-bearer, died 1979. Was with his brother 'Fadje' in the skiff *Mary*. Between the wars, worked his own boat, the *Ina*, a 36-ft skiff, carvel-built at Port Bannatyne. Fished until aged 70, his last berth being with Archie Kerr on the *Pride of the Clyde*. Known as Hughie 'Nelly'. [1974, 1975, 1976]

Robert McGown*, b 1902, Campbeltown. Went to fishing in 1916 with Jock Taylor in the *Daisy* of Dalintober. Had the *Felicia* built in 1927 by Reekie, St Monans. He was a Chairman of the Campbeltown branch of the Clyde Fishermen's Association. [1974]

Duncan MacInnes, b 1925, Bunavullin, Eriskay. Went to the Merchant Navy in 1941. Joined the crew of the Eriskay ring-netter *Lady of Fatima* – in which he was a shareholder – around 1947 and fished intermittently until c 1967. Is now retired and living in Kinlochleven. [2000]

John McIntyre*, b 1911, Campbeltown. His earliest berth was in 1925 with John 'Plimsoll' Gilchrist in the *Catherine and Agnes*. Joined Robert Robertson's crews in 1930 and served on the *Kestrel*. Was made skipper of the *King Fisher* after Robertson retired through ill-health. [1974, 1976]

George McMillan, b 1944, Ardrishaig. His father was from Campbeltown, but his mother belonged to the Bruce fishing family in Ardrishaig. Went to fishing in 1960 in the *Nobles Again*. After five years, moved to Tarbert and joined the *Fionnaghal*, followed by the *Nancy Glen*. Had his own 40-footer, the *Provider*, for a few years, after which he left the fishing. Captained the fishery research vessel, *Calanus*. [2000]

David McNaughton, b 1926, Campbeltown. Son of a fisherman, Daniel McNaughton, and nephew of Archibald 'Baldy' Stewart. Went to fishing, aged 14, and left the job in 1952, having crewed on the *Lily, Nobles, Monsoon, Annie, Royal Burghs* and *Bluebird*. Was aboard fishery protection vessels and then car-ferries until his retirement through ill health. [1999]

Hugh McPhee, b 1941, Alloway, but went to live in Maidens as a boy. A gardener's son, he went to fishing at the age of 16 in Billy Sloan's *Wistaria* and was there for 16 years. Thereafter, he had the *Freedom* with Andy Alexander, then on his own. Now in semi-retirement, he fishes the second *Freedom*, with his son David, and tends a flock of Texel sheep.

Duncan McSporran*, b 1888, Dalintober. Went to the fishing in 1905. Skippered first the *Lily* and then – just after the Second World War – the *Nobles*, leaving in 1950 to join Willie McArthur in the *Mary McLean*, from which he retired in 1967. [1974]

Francis McWhirter, b 1927, Campbeltown. His first berth was in 1943 in the *Gratitude* with Jock Meenan. Was subsequently on the *Golden Dawn* and the *Regina Maris*, before going ashore to work in 1955. Son of Campbeltown boat-owner and skipper, John McWhirter. [1999]

Angus Martin*, b 1895, Dalintober. Went to fishing in 1910 in his father's skiff, the *Elm*. Bought the skiff *Fame* from his uncle, Duncan Martin, in 1935. In 1948, had the *Endeavour* built at Dickie's of Tarbert and fished her with his sons until 1954. His first year in the North was with Murdoch Weir in the *Shenandoah*. [1974]

Henry Martin*, b 1891, Dalintober. Served his time as a blacksmith at Campbeltown Shipyard before taking up the fishing seriously. Was with his father, Duncan Martin, in the skiff *Fame*, fishing from Dalintober, until the boat was sold in 1935. Thereafter, in common with all other Dalintober fishermen who survived the skiff era, he found employment in modern ring-netters, including the *Kestrel, Enterprise, Maureen* and *Margaret Hamilton*, of Campbeltown, and the *Cluaran* of Carradale. [1974, 1975]

Denis Meenan, b 1926, Campbeltown. His first berth was in the *Busy Bee* in 1941; afterwards with his uncle Jock Meenan in the *Gratitude*. He was in the Navy from 1945 until 1948, when he joined the *Stella Maris*, launched that year for him and his brother Jim, who died in 1967. Owned further boats named *Stella Maris*. Retired in 1986. [1998]

Jim Munro, b 1946, a native of Dunure but lives in Troon. At his father's insistence, served an apprenticeship – as a joiner – before going to sea at the age of 21 in Billy Gibson's *Britannia*. Skipper-owned the *Nimrod, Strathnairn* and finally the *Heroine* before going ashore in 1996 to work as a self-employed joiner. [2000]

Johnny Munro, b 1922, Dunure. His first berth, after leaving school, was with the Grieves' *Mary Munro*. After war service, skippered several family boats – neighbouring his brother Sandy – finishing up on the *New Dawn*, from which he retired in 1987. [1999]

Archibald Paterson, b 1925, Carradale. He left school in June 1939, a month before his 14th birthday, and joined the crew of the *Rolling Wave*, skippered by his cousin 'Red' Robert Paterson. After a spell in Willie McIntosh's *Stella Maris*, he skippered the Fairlie-built *Harvest Queen* – which he owned jointly with Donald McNicol – from her launch in 1949 until his retirement. [2000]

Tommy Ralston, b 1935, Campbeltown. His first berth was aboard his father's boat, the *Golden Fleece* (previously the *Bonito* of Dunure) in 1950. Joined the Mallaig ringer, *Jessie Alice*, c. 1956, and fished from that port – where he married and settled – for about 10 years. Afterwards became a fish-buyer. Was coxswain of Mallaig lifeboat. Author of two books, *My Captains* (1995) and *To the Edge* (1997). [1999, 2000]

Duncan Ritchie, b 1926, Carradale. Went to fishing at age of 13, having been given an exemption from school at the outbreak of war. Was in the *Florentine* then the *Thalassa*, before himself going off to the war. Joined the *Betty* in 1947 and was afterwards in the new-built *Acacia* from 1949 to 1952, when he left the fishing. Had a number of jobs before going into the kippering business in Rothesay with his brother Neil in 1957. He retired in 1973 and now lives in his native Carradale. [1999]

Robert Ross, Tarbert, b 1926. First went to fishing in 1940, aged 14, aboard 'Poogie' McDougall's *Flying Fish*. From 1949 to 1952, was with the McDougalls' *Mairearad*, his main experience of the North fishing. Part-owned and skippered the *Dalriada*, built in 1954 for ring-netting and seine-netting, and later acquired the *Sunbeam*. He retired in 1982, but acted as a relief skipper until 1990. [1998, 1999, 2000]

Neil Short, b 1917, Campbeltown. A son of prominent boat-owner and skipper, John Short. In the 1930s, fished in the *Nulli Secundus* and *King Fisher*, was in the *King Bird* in the late 1940s and 1950s. Stopped fishing in the 1960s and moved to Glasgow, where he worked for the Bergius-Kelvin engine company, retiring in 1982. [1998, 1999, 2000]

Matthew Sloan, b 1917, Maidens, son of Tommy Sloan. Went to fishing first in the family ringer, *Veronica*, in 1931. After war service, he and his brother Billy had the first *Wistaria* built, then bought, second-hand from Girvan, the *Bairn's Pride*, his first regular command. The *Watchful* was built in 1959 and Matt skippered her. In 1965 a new *Wistaria* was built, which Billy skippered. Matt retired in 1973. [1976, 1999, 2000]

Archibald Stewart*, b 1889, Campbeltown. Was with John Short in the Loch Fyne Skiff *Mary Graham* and crewed on later Short boats. Skippered Robert Robertson's *King Bird* and, later, Jim Daniels's *Lily* and *Nobles*. He and his sons had the *Boy Danny* built by Miller, St Monans, in 1948. 'Baldy' was one of the great characters in the Campbeltown fishing fraternity, rivalled in his exploits by 'Tit' Ralston alone. [1974]

APPENDIX 2
THE LITTLE PLACES

Many of these features – which belong predominantly on the West Shore – were small and associated with ring-net hauls. The names themselves were mostly coined by the Clyde fishermen. There were many other place-names in use, but these were well-established – picked up from charts or from native fishermen – and appear on the map at the front of this book. The native lore connected with certain of these names below came from Mr Duncan MacInnes, who also provided the alternative native names, which Mr Ian A Fraser of The School of Scottish Studies, Edinburgh, kindly rendered into written Gaelic.

Bay Harty. Fishermen's version of Hartabhagh, which derives from Old Norse *harta-vagr*, 'deer-bay', though, as Ian Fraser points out, 'This doesn't necessarily mean that deer were present, but that there were deer-like, or antler-like shapes in the area'.

Billy's Bight/Bicht. Immediately south of Loch Eynort. Sometimes linked with Billy Sloan of the Maidens, but more likely to commemorate the Kyleakin skipper, Billy Finlayson of the *Castle Moil*, who often fished there, particularly in early summer. Locally, *Bagh a' Ghlinne Mhóir*, Bay of the Big Glen.

Bobby Shaun/Shand Buoy. Corrupted name of the buoyed rock which is 'Bo Vich Chuan' on Admiralty charts and which possibly represents *Bogha Mhic Chuimhein*, 'MacQueen's Rock'.

The Blower. A rock at Brevig, Barra, which spouts – or blows – water into the air in certain sea conditions.

The Light at Calvay. The Lighthouse at Calvay Island, at the entrance to Loch Boisdale.

The Cleft Rock. A split in the rock – locally known as *Leum MhicNeacaill*, 'Nicolson's Leap' – between Corodale and Shepherd's Bight. Traditionally associated with a farm-boy called Nicolson who got his master's daughter pregnant and was pursued and cornered at that place. The punishment was to be castration, but the laird made a deal with the boy, that if he could leap across the fissure he would be released unharmed. The boy succeeded.

Davie's Hole. In Loch Skiport, from a big ring of herring David Wood of Pittenweem had in there with the *Hope*. Also called **MacCormack's Bight**.

Dirty Point. Kilmory Point, on the north end of Rum, from the nasty configuration of rocks there.

The Drain. Up beyond Lochboisdale Quay, a gut down which the tide pours 'like a river'.

The Duff. A big lump of rock, on the north side of Shepherd's Bight, shaped like a plum duff. Associated with Sammy Gemmell, who always liked to get his 'Hallowe'en oot the Duff', ie take a good fishing out of the haul on 31 October.

The Duke's Rock. The rock in Eriskay Sound on which Charlie 'Duke' Durnin's *Bluebird* went aground (p 110). Also **Bluebird Rock** and **Charlie Durnin's Rock**. The native name was evidently *Sgeir Rudha Dubh*, 'Reef of the Black Headland'.

Gull Rock. About 60 yards off the south-east coast of Eriskay. Duncan MacInnes gives the native name as *Sgeir Liath*, or 'Blue Rock', and comments that it was 'always white with gulls whenever there was herring around".

Hound Sound. A corruption of Haun, the anchorage on the north end of Eriskay. The Campbeltown fishermen's name for Eriskay Sound.

The Kettle, Kettle Pool or Kettle Drum. An enclosed bay, much used as an anchorage, on the south side of Loch Skiport.

Kruger's Bight. A bay on the south side of Gighay named after Jimmy 'Kruger' McCreath of Girvan, who had a big ring of herring there between the wars. Also on the north-west side of the Heisgeir (p 57).

The Labster Pot. Outside the Kettle. Lobster keep-ponds had been built there by Angus MacLellan, a native of Mallaig, popularly known as the 'Yank'.

The Lion. A rock on the north-east coast of Canna, below Compass Hill, likened in shape to a lion. The Mallaig fishermen saw it differently and named it The Sheep, while the Ordnance Survey recorded it as *An t-Each*, 'The Horse'. **The Stac** was close by.

The Lum Hat. A perched rock, resembling a tall hat, at the mouth of Barra Sound.

Moonlight Bay. North of Loch Eynort. Associated with the McDougall 'Ghosts' of Tarbert. The native name was *Bagh Theilibreig*.

Politician Rock. Off Roshinish Point, on the north-east end of Eriskay, where the ship *Politician* was famously wrecked, in 1941, with a cargo which included some 25,000 cases of blended whisky, an estimated 5,000 of which were unofficially salvaged before Customs and Police officers intervened. The incident was turned into the novel, *Whisky Galore*, by Compton Mackenzie, and further popularised in a film, shot on Barra in 1948. 'Baldy' Stewart always claimed to have benefited from the bonanza. Earlier known to local fishermen as *Roc Ceann Calbhaigh*, or Calvay Head Rock. A *roc* in Gaelic is a sunken rock with tangle growing on it.

Rowlin Bey. 'Rolling Bay' – Moonen Bay, Skye, from the motion of the sea there.

Shepherd's Bight. Directly south of Loch Skiport. A shepherd's house stands above the bay.

Shit Creek. South of the bight at Calvay Island, so named because when a net was shot there it got loaded with seaweed. Native fishermen knew it as *Bagh a' Chamais*.

Sword Bay. Sword-shaped, being wide at the entrance and narrow beyond. North of Bay Harty.

Tarry's Bight. A bay north of Loch Boisdale, commemorating Andy 'Tarry' McCrindle of Girvan, though other Clyde fishermen had earlier worked the bay.

Telephone /Telegraph Bay. Between Castlebay and Brevig, where a telephone cable comes ashore.

Weaver's Castle. The castle, which commands the entrance to Barra Sound, is a very obvious landmark and is connected in legend with a pirate whose stronghold it was.

The Wine Glass. On Pabbay; so-called because viewed from a certain angle and from the correct distance off, sandy strips in the grass resembled a wineglass.

REFERENCES

1. A. Martin, *The Ring-Net Fishermen*, 1981, pp 196-7.
2. *Fishery Board of Scotland Annual Report* 1933, p 19.
3. I. Gemmell, Jan 1999.
4. T. Ralston, 19 March 2000.
5. Quoted in F. Thompson, *The Highlands and Islands*, London, 1974, p 299
6. *Campbeltown Courier*, 18 Jan, 25 Jan & 8 Feb 1968.
7 J.L. Campbell, *Canna: The Story of a Hebridean Island*, 1994, p 235.
8. Neil McDougall, 1 April 2000.
9. Mike Hughes, *The Hebrides at War*, 1998.

BOOKS REFERRED TO DURING THE COMPILATION OF THIS WORK

Clyde Cruising Club Sailing Directory: West Coast of Scotland, Glasgow, 1947.
MacInnes, A E: *Eriskay Where I Was Born*, Edinburgh, 1997.
Martin, A: *Fishing and Whaling*, Edinburgh, 1995.
Newton, N: *The Shell Guide to the Islands of Britain*, Newton Abbot, 1992.
Ralston, T: *My Captains*, Aberdeen, 1995.

GLOSSARY

A – I
aa – all
aafu – awful
abaird – aboard
aboord – aboard
aboot – about
ach – an interjection expressing
    exasperation, contempt, etc
aff – off
afore – before
agane – again
aheid – ahead
apairt – apart
atween – between
aucht – anything
aw – all
awa – away, gone
awfu – awful

bail – discharge, specifically fish
    from a net
bargin – (presumably) packing
bark – to tan nets with the preserva-
    tive, cutch
barrel – a measurement of drift-nets,
    reckoned at about 90 yards (82.30
    m) or roughly what a barrel
    would hold
bate – bet
bech – a roar, shout
belt – a blow
bend – the heavy rubbing-strake on
    a boat's side
bey – bay
bicht – bight, bay
biled – boiled
birlt – turned
boat – to haul aboard the boat
bow – buoy
brailing – discharging a catch from
    ring-net

braw – fine
breid – bread
burnin – sea-phosphorescence

cailleach – old woman
canna – cannot
canny – careful, cautious
cant – turn
carlins – deck-beams
cerry – carry
chappie – 'Chappie' was one of the
    earliest brands of tinned pet-foods
    on the British market, appearing
    in the 1930s
cloakin – clocking or incubating
cou'na – couldn't
cowld – cold
cran – a measurement of ungutted
    herring, equivalent to a barrel (see
    also p 81)

dae – do
daein – doing
daud – a lump
didnae – didn't
dinna – didn't
disna – doesn't
divide – a share, specifically of boat's
    earnings; to share
doin – rough treatment; severe
    damage to fishing gear
dooker – a 'ducker', or diving bird;
    in Tarbert, specifically the
    guillemot
doon – down
doot – doubt
drap – drop
dry – of herring, when a ring-net bag
    has been hauled in as far as it can
    be and the catch is floundering
    almost literally in a dry state; also

when a bulk of herring rises on
  the surface and 'plays the sea dry'
durty – dirty

eether – either
efter – after
efternoon – afternoon
en – end
erse – arse
everwho – whoever
eye – shoal (of fish)

fadom – fathom (6ft or 1.83 m)
fae – from
faither – father
fankled – tangled
feel – sense, smell
feenished – finished
fella – fellow
fir – for
forby – besides
forrad, forrid – forward
fou – full (pronounced 'foo')
fower – four
fricht – fright
furrid, furrit – forward
furst – first

gable – either end of a ring-net; also
  known as the 'lug'
gan – going
garrin – playing loudly (Gael *gàir*, a
  roar or any loud noise)
gaun – going
gether – gather
gey – rather
gie – give
gless – glass
gloaming – evening
goat – got
gonny – going to
greetin – weeping
grun – ground
guid – good

hadnae – hadn't
haev – have
hame – home

han – hand
hanna – hadn't
heckle – a hackle, or mass of jagged
  rocks
heid – head
herried – harried
hingin – hanging
hissel – himself
hoose – house
hoot – what
howld – (fish-)hold
hunder, hunner – hundred
huvnae – haven't

intae – into
ir – are

jeest, jist – just

keekin – peeking
ken – know
kent – knew
kinna – kind of
kit – a small barrel in which herring
  were cured

laik – like
lea – leave
licht – light
lik – like
loas – lose
loast – lost
lodded – loaded
luck – look

ma – my
mair – more
mashed – enmeshed
moarnin – morning
mony – many
mooth – mouth

nabby – a round-sterned, lug-sailed
  boat which evolved on the eastern
  side of the Firth of Clyde in the
  18th century
naethin – nothing
naewhere – nowhere

nane – none
naw – no, not
neb – beak
neebor – neighbour
nee'na – needn't
nicht – night
no – not
noo – now

o – of
oan – on
onythin – anything
oor – our, hour
oot – out
ould – old
ower – over
oxters – armpits

pintle – the iron pin on to which a
    boat's rudder was shipped
pittin – putting
plestered – plastered
podlie – a half-grown saithe
poke – bag
pou – pull (pronounced 'poo')
puckle – a little

quarter – either side of a boat, abaft
    the beam

rasher – a fry-up
redd – clear, sort
richt – right
ring – to shoot a ring-net; a ring-net
    shot circularly
roon, roond – round
roost – rust
rowl – roll
rummellin – knocking violently
rumped – bounced

saicond – second
sail-fish – basking-shark
sate – seat
scart – cormorant or shag
scuttle – the opening in the forecastle
    hatch
seck – sake

seeventy – seventy
shooder – shoulder
shot – to shoot, or set, fishing gear; a
    catch of fish
shouldnae, shou'nae – shouldn't
sicht – sight
skair – a reef (Gaelic *sgeir*)
skelf – splinter
skiddoag – a special boat-hook for
    catching end of ring-net (chiefly
    Campbeltown, Carradale)
skift – skiff
sling – the bag section of a ring-net
sma – small
snasters – sweetmeats (derisory)
soalid – solid
sole(s) – the foot, or bottom, of a net
soomed – swam
soon – sound
sorta – sort of
spiled – spoiled
spot, spoat – a shoal of fish
stannin – standing
sternsheets – the space in the stern of
    a skiff, aft of the rowing-beams
    and forward of the steering-beam,
    where the steersman sat; in Loch
    Fyne Skiffs, generally boarded
    over, and, after the introduction
    of motor-power, the accommoda-
    tion for the engine
stopped – lashed with 'stoppers' or
    bickets
sweepline – the rope made fast to the
    end of the net for towing it

tae – to
ta'en – taken
tap – top
tellt – told
Teuchter – Highlander
thegither – together
themorra – tomorrow
therty – thirty
they – these
thir – their
thole-pin – one of two pins forming a
    rowlock, within which the oar is

worked

thonder – yonder

thoosan/d – thousand

thrott – throat

touch – a lucrative catch

traal – trawl, an early name for the
ring-net

twa – two

train – a fleet of drift-nets

waant – want

waatch – watch

wan – one

wance – once

watter – water

wey – way

whar, whaur – where

wheen – a number of anything

whit – what

whoot – what

wi – with

widnae – wouldn't

wid've – would've

wile – wild, terrible

win – wind

winda – window

winky – lit end-buoy of ring-net,
from its blinking

winna, winnae – wouldn't

wir – were, our

wirna – weren't

wis – was

wisna – wasn't

winna – wouldn't

wouldnae – wouldn't

ye – you

yer – your

yin – one

yit – yet

youse – you (plural)

INDEXES

Post-1920 Ring-Netters

Ring-Net Fishermen Mentioned

112, 131, 168
MacDonald, Willie, 29, 83, 157–8
McDougalls of Tarbert, 17, 47, 64–5, 72, 102, 160
McDougall, Alec 'Butcher', 97
McDougall, Alec 'Aleca', 148
McDougall, Archie, 17, 88, 148, 161
McDougall, Donald Sr, 17
McDougall, Donald Jr, 17, 84, 88, 101, 156
McDougall, Duncan 'Dunks', 129
McDougall, John 'Doods', 103
McDougall, Matthew, 61, 93, 106, 117
McDougall, Neil, 16, 91, 99, 117, 152, 161
McDougall, Peter, Sr, 17, 88, 159
McDougall, Peter, Jr, 17, 95, 146, 169
McEwan, Eddie, 22, 23, 162
MacFarlane, Eoghan, 52
MacFarlane, Hugh, 7, 8, 11, 12, 16, 104, 126, 137, 147, 149
MacFarlane, John, 8
MacFarlane, Neil, 12
McGougan, Malcolm, 72, 97
McGown, Robert, MBE, 14, 44, 72
MacInnes, Duncan, 43, 60–1, 65, 86, 93–4, 125, 133, 155
MacInnes, 'Black' John, 94, 155
MacInnes, Norman, 61, 93–4, 133
McIntosh, Denis, 118, 129
McIntosh, Donald, 9
McIntyre, George, 92
McIntyre, Jock, 28, 56, 118, 128, 164
McIntyre, Willie, 27–8
MacIsaac, Angus, 93, 124
McKay, Archie, 8
McKay, Denis, 8
McKay, Pat, 54, 58, 153, 162
McKenzie, Neil, 18
McKenzie, Willie, 90
McKinlay, John, 30, 63
McKinlay, Sandy, 156
MacKinnons of Eriskay, 5, 40, 161
McKinnon, Archie, 88
MacKinnon, Calum, 49, 70–1, 119, 168
McKinven, James, 62
McLean, Danny, 156
McLean, James, 115
McLean, Malcolm, 30
McLean, Neil 'Teedlety', 8
McLean, Neil, son of James, 21
McLean, Neilly, 22
McMillan, Bobby, 145
McMillan, Donald, 99

McMillan, George, 133
McMillan, Hector, 103
McMillan, Johnny, 51, 98–9
McNaughton, Dan, 46
McNaughton, David, 13, 30, 37–8, 46, 63, 73, 83, 114, 120, 123, 130, 132, 140, 145, 152
McPhee, Hugh, 46–8, 63, 100, 127, 146
McSporran, Duncan, 2, 8, 37–8, 46, 74, 79, 123
McWhirter, Francis, 111, 120, 130, 134, 158, 159
Mansons of Mallaig, 5, 10, 19, 59, 75, 133
Manson, Jim, 60, 98, 155
Martin, Alister, 88
Martin, Angus, 79, 87
Martin, Henry, 28, 90, 148
Mathieson, Archie 'Try', 18
Meenan, Denis, 22, 50, 52, 67, 90, 92, 130, 134, 137, 158, 159, 168
Meenan, James, 134
Meenan, Jim, 72, 92, 168
Meenan, Jock, 44, 92, 118, 159
Mitchell, Ian, 164
Morans, Bob, 112, 155
Munro, Jim, 17, 18, 54, 136, 140, 167
Munro, Johnny, 58, 62, 74, 100
Munro, Mungo, 54
Munro, Sandy, 58, 74
Munro, Willie, 139
Murdoch, Duncan, 102

Newlands, George, 85

Paterson, Archie, 14, 15, 51–2, 74, 91, 98–100, 118, 128, 129, 151, 164, 165
Paterson, Davie, 98
Paterson, Donald 'Fergie', 165
Paterson, Dugald, 91, 98, 99, 151
Paterson, Robert, 128, 151

Rae, Alex, 29
Ralston, Tommy Sr, 58, 116, 128, 133, 138, 146, 163
Ralston, Tommy Jr, 10, 33, 62, 78, 80, 120, 123, 137, 140, 142, 147
Reid, 'Rice', 10
Ritchie, Duncan, 61, 70, 97, 107, 114, 115, 124, 129, 132, 138, 143–4
Robertson, Andrew 'Knuckler', 152
Robertson, James 'Knuckler, 18
Robertson, James 'Gypsy', 164
Robertson, Peter, 73

General